Discover Verbal Reasonin

Frequently Asked Questions For Adults

What is this book about?

Discover Verbal Reasoning is in level one of the *Practise & Pass 11+* series. It is a workbook for students who are going to take an 11+ test or school entrance exam that includes a verbal reasoning section. In this book I introduce them to 15 key types of question they'll typically face in the exams and provide 300 questions to practise.

I provide coaching for students throughout the book. I talk them through the whole process from answering questions to helping them understand their mistakes, giving them a firm understanding of the basics.

What is verbal reasoning?

Verbal reasoning is problem-solving using language, vocabulary and sometimes mathematical skills. There are many different types of verbal reasoning question and this book looks at the 15 most common.

How do I use this book?

This book is divided into bite-sized lessons for the student to work through. Each lesson covers a specific type of question and is set up in the same way:

1. I explain the question type, giving the student an understanding of what they need to know.

2. I provide a worked example or two to show how the question type is best tackled.

   (Note: I do recommend that an adult reads through the explanation and example(s) with the student to ensure they have a firm understanding of what is required.)

3. When ready, the student should work through the first set of practice questions on their own.

4. The answers to the questions are inserted on the following page. Once the student has completed the practice questions they can mark their answers themselves.

5. After the answers I provide a summary of what the student's score means and give hints on how to improve it, if needs be.

   (Note: the student should discuss any errors and talk through the hints together with an adult so that any problems are dealt with straight away.)

6. Next, there is a second set of practice questions. I suggest that the student should only work on these when they understand why they made mistakes first-time around.

   Important: this second set of questions should be marked by an adult and the answers can be found on pages 127 and 128. You might want to cut these out of the book so the temptation for the student to take a peek is removed!

7. Finally, there is a score sheet on page 124 which should be completed after each lesson to keep a record of progress. This can be used to identify those question types the student needs to practise more.

   (Note: occasionally I will include a question that hasn't been explained in the lesson. This is by design: the student will very likely come up against a question they are not familiar with in the actual test so it's important that they get used to applying the knowledge they have to work out the right answer.)

Why does this book feature multiple choice answers?

Multiple choice answers are becoming the most common format for the 11+. This means that four or five possible answers are given for each question and they are presented to the student in a grid format. To answer the question correctly the student has to put a horizontal line in the empty box next to the correct answer.

⇨ It's important that students learn to use these answer grids correctly from the outset so they avoid making common errors, such as marking the wrong box or accidentally missing out questions.

⇨ You should make sure you find out from the examination centre whether the multiple choice format will be used in the final exam so you're confident that the student is doing the right preparation.

When should the student start to prepare for the exam and how often should they practise?

The sooner the student starts to prepare for the exam the better. Realistically, I suggest there should be a full year's run-up to the test so that the student has a chance to practise all of the subject areas and question types that might appear in the exam, without having to study for hours and hours each week. This means working through all three levels of the *Practise & Pass 11+* series (this book is in level one of the series) at a steady and realistic pace.

For this book I recommend students work at the pace of one lesson a week which means 15 weeks in total. However, if a student is able, there is nothing to stop them moving through the book at a quicker pace.

What's the best way for a student to study?

⇨ It's important that the student gets used to a test-type environment so make sure there's a clear space to work in, with no distractions. The TV and all music should be switched off, the student should be sat at a table and there should be a clock in clear view so that they can time themselves.

⇨ Students should use a pencil to answer the questions and have an eraser and some scrap paper to hand which they can use for any workings out.

(Note: I highly recommend that the student avoid practising on the same days that they have school homework and that they also have other extra-curricular activities – this means they have other outlets for their energies and don't become overworked, stressed or too bored with the practice.)

How quickly should a student answer the questions?

I have suggested timings for each lesson but do note that, as this book is in level one of the series, the timings here are more generous than they will be in the actual exam. At this stage students should concentrate on becoming familiar with the question types and their methods – they can ignore the timings for the time-being if they wish.

Once students are used to the questions they can then practise speeding up. At level two of the series I do expect the students to be up to speed and they should follow the timings far more closely (this way they are prepared to work at a 'real time' pace that matches the actual exam).

What score should the student be aiming for?

Remember that 11+ tests and entrance exams are tough to pass. I have written this book to reflect that fact, so it is unlikely that the student will sail through the book scoring 100% in each lesson!

After the first set of practice questions in every lesson, I have given a target score for that particular question type – this is based on my experience of teaching them year on year and should help you assess how the student is doing, and what areas, if any, need work. I also include helpful tips on how students can improve, and would recommend they use the 'vocabulary builders'.

I should add that the scores here in no way indicate whether the student will definitely pass or fail the exam; they are only here as a guide.

What are the 'vocabulary builders'?

There are a few vocabulary builder exercises throughout this book. These are 'just for fun' extra tasks to help improve the student's vocabulary. In addition to these, one of the best ways for students to help prepare for the examination is to read regularly. The better their vocabulary, the better they are likely to cope with the questions in the actual exam.

What should I do once this book is completed?

This book is just the start; I recommend that you move on to level two of the series: *Develop Verbal Reasoning*. In level two there are many more practice questions covering more question types and trickier versions of questions that stretch the student further and improve their familiarity with what's expected from them on test day. There is also further advice from me on how students can improve their scores and speed up their work, ensuring they are fully prepared for test day.

LESSON 1 Finding Hidden Words

In this exercise you'll need to find the <u>four</u>-letter word that is hidden in each sentence. The word will be formed from the letters at the end of one word and the beginning of the next.

There are two rules you need to remember for this kind of question: firstly, the letters must remain in the same order. Secondly, a word found entirely in one word isn't a correct answer. Look at the example below.

Example

The children wore hats and coats.

The hidden word is <u>sand</u> because it's formed using letters from two words and it has four letters.

For your answer you'll need to mark the two words which hide the word: <u>hats and</u>.

HELPFUL HINTS

- Begin by looking at the gaps between the words. Take three letters from the end of the word on the left and one from the beginning of the word next to it. If those four letters don't make a word, move across until all the possible letter combinations have been tested.

For example, with the words: The children

First try	<u>The</u> children	'Thec' isn't a word.
Next try	Th<u>e c</u>hildren	'hech' isn't a word.
Next try	Th<u>e ch</u>ildren	'echi' isn't a word.

As there is no word hidden between these two words you should move on to the next two words in the sentence to try to find the answer.

- Some letters are unlikely to be found next to each other in words. Look at the words 'played with' – there aren't many words with 'd' and 'w' together so you can skip that gap and come back to it only if a word can't be found elsewhere. This will save you valuable time. This is also true for 'with bats' – do you know many words with an 'h' and a 'b' together?

- Don't fall into the one-word trap. The word 'play' can be found in the word 'played' but it isn't a correct answer because it does not span two words.

5

LESSON 1 PART 1

My Time	My Score

Now look at the questions below. When you've found the two words with which you can make a new word, mark your answer on the opposite page. Try to do each question as quickly as you can and make sure you finish them all. When you've finished, write down the time you took in the box at the top.

You have 10 minutes to complete this task, so work quickly!

1 His top mark is fifty seven.

2 Take care not to spill ink.

3 She listened to him with empathy.

4 The candle flame attracts unwary moths.

5 Hail and snow kept falling heavily.

6 The local grocer sold ripe fruit.

7 Some story books end too abruptly.

8 Please also attempt the difficult questions.

9 The boy unluckily twisted his ankle.

10 They felt terribly stiff all day.

LESSON 1 PART 1: ANSWER SHEET

Mark your answer by putting a horizontal line in one of the boxes, as in the example below.

Example:

The children	▢
children wore	▢
wore hats	▢
hats and	▬
and coats	▢

1

His top	▢
top mark	▢
mark is	▢
is fifty	▢
fifty seven	▢

2

Take care	▢
care not	▢
not to	▢
to spill	▢
spill ink	▢

3

She listened	▢
listened to	▢
to him	▢
him with	▢
with empathy	▢

4

The candle	▢
candle flame	▢
flame attracts	▢
attracts unwary	▢
unwary moths	▢

5

Hail and	▢
and snow	▢
snow kept	▢
kept falling	▢
falling heavily	▢

6

The local	▢
local grocer	▢
grocer sold	▢
sold ripe	▢
ripe fruit	▢

7

Some story	▢
story books	▢
books end	▢
end too	▢
too abruptly	▢

8

Please also	▢
also attempt	▢
attempt the	▢
the difficult	▢
difficult questions	▢

9

The boy	▢
boy unluckily	▢
unluckily twisted	▢
twisted his	▢
his ankle	▢

10

They felt	▢
felt terribly	▢
terribly stiff	▢
stiff all	▢
all day	▢

How Did You Do?
Let's Find Out!

Here are the correct answers. You may mark your answers to these questions yourself. The words that were hidden are underlined and listed on the right.

1	His top	<u>stop</u>
2	spill ink	<u>link</u>
3	with empathy	<u>them</u> or <u>hemp</u>
4	flame attracts	<u>meat</u>
5	Hail and	<u>land</u>
6	sold ripe	<u>drip</u>
7	books end	<u>send</u>
8	Please also	<u>seal</u>
9	his ankle	<u>sank</u>
10	stiff all	<u>fall</u>

If you scored 8 or more out of 10

This is great! Move on to the next set of questions and see if you can continue your good work, but do look at the words you got wrong to help you improve.

If you scored 5 to 7 out of 10

This is an okay score but read the following advice before moving on to the next set of questions.

⇨ Look at the answers. You should know all of these words. If you don't, you'll find it helpful to spend more time reading to improve your vocabulary. Also read the vocabulary builders (see pages 44, 60, 92, 100 and 116), which aim to help you learn new words. You'll need to look up the words in a dictionary and practise using them in a sentence of your own.

⇨ Did you spell any words wrongly? For example, in question 6 some students think the two words 'The local' spells the word 'helo'. But the correct spelling is 'hello'. If you find you're spelling fairly common words incorrectly, spend more time practising your spelling.

If you scored fewer than 5 out of 10

Fewer than 5 is a score which you need to improve. Read the suggestions that follow before moving on to the next set of questions.

⇨ Do you understand what you have to do? If not, ask an adult to read the instructions and go through the example with you again. Then take another look at your answers and see if you can correct them.

⇨ Do you understand how to mark your answers on the answer sheet? Sometimes students make mistakes here because they haven't answered questions in this way before. Again, ask an adult to show you how to mark the answers correctly. Then look at the questions once more and answer them again.

⇨ If you don't recognise some of the words or you misspelled them, make sure you practise spelling common words. Also, try to read regularly at home (that means every night).

⇨ Look at the vocabulary builders (pages 44, 60, 92, 100 and 116) to help you with new words.

LESSON 1 PART 2

My Time

My Score

This time you'll need to watch out for letters that change their sounds when put together. I might have included a few of these just to keep you on your toes! Look at the example first.

Example

They should start their wor<u>k now</u>.

Do you see how the sounds changed? The hard 'k' in 'work' becomes silent in 'know'. The vowel sound of 'now' also changed. Be careful with these.

You have 10 minutes to complete this task, so work quickly! When you've finished, ask an adult to mark your answers.

1 Her coat ripped on the tree.

2 She bought a lovely new hat.

3 They listened to him with interest.

4 Please smile while addressing the audience.

5 The animals played outside all day.

6 To what extent did you understand?

7 Some while after that they departed.

8 The gentle lamb entered the field.

9 The door opened from the inside.

10 We are permitted to watch television.

LESSON 1 PART 2: ANSWER SHEET

Mark your answer by putting a horizontal line in one of the boxes, as in the example below.

Example:

They should	☐
should start	☐
start their	☐
their work	☐
work now	▬

1

Her coat	☐
coat ripped	☐
ripped on	☐
on the	☐
the tree	☐

2

She bought	☐
bought a	☐
a lovely	☐
lovely new	☐
new hat	☐

3

They listened	☐
listened to	☐
to him	☐
him with	☐
with interest	☐

4

Please smile	☐
smile while	☐
while addressing	☐
addressing the	☐
the audience	☐

5

The animals	☐
animals played	☐
played outside	☐
outside all	☐
all day	☐

6

To what	☐
what extent	☐
extent did	☐
did you	☐
you understand	☐

7

Some while	☐
while after	☐
after that	☐
that they	☐
they departed	☐

8

The gentle	☐
gentle lamb	☐
lamb entered	☐
entered the	☐
the field	☐

9

The door	☐
door opened	☐
opened from	☐
from the	☐
the inside	☐

10

We are	☐
are permitted	☐
permitted to	☐
to watch	☐
watch television	☐

LESSON 2 Filling in the Missing Three-Letter Word

In this exercise you'll see a word in CAPITAL letters in every sentence. This word has been shortened by removing <u>three</u> of its letters. You'll need to work out which three letters have been removed. These letters will spell a word and this three-letter word will be your answer. (Note that you don't need to juggle the letters about or add any more letters to make a proper word, they are already in the correct order.)

Example

Try to keep your HWRITING neat and tidy.

In this sentence, the word HWRITING isn't correct. Try to think what word would make sense in the sentence.

The word should be <u>H</u>AN<u>D</u>WRITING. The missing letters are <u>AND</u>. Note how this spells the simple three-letter word 'and'. This is the word you'll need to mark on your answer sheet.

HELPFUL HINTS

- The three missing letters always spell a word and they are always kept in the correct order. Read the sentence at normal pace and you'll be able work out what the shortened word should be quite quickly.

- Always think of which word would make sense in the context of the sentence.

- If you want to double check your answer, write the word out in full and cross off the letters you have already been given. This should leave you with the correct three-letter word.

LESSON 2 PART 1

My Time	My Score

Now look at the questions below. When you've found the answer, mark it on the opposite page. Try to do each question as quickly as you can, and make sure you complete them all. When you've finished write down the time you took in the box at the top.

You have 10 minutes to complete this task, so work quickly!

1 The footballer SCO a goal.

2 There were two rare mountain GORAS at the zoo.

3 The children SPLED water in the swimming pool.

4 The injured lady was rushed to HOSAL.

5 After the storm we could see a beautiful RAIN.

6 Violin PRICE takes place after school on a Wednesday.

7 We ATTED football training last week.

8 There were only three items in the shopping BET.

9 Be careful when you walk up the steep STCASE.

10 After his run he took a long, warm SER.

LESSON 2 PART 1: ANSWER SHEET

Mark your answer by putting a horizontal line in one of the boxes, as in the example below.

Example:

```
END  ▭
AND  ▬
ARE  ▭
OUR  ▭
ERE  ▭
```

1
```
ORE  ▭
ARE  ▭
RED  ▭
WED  ▭
BED  ▭
```

2
```
ALL  ▭
ILL  ▭
AGE  ▭
APE  ▭
ARE  ▭
```

3
```
IMP  ▭
ASH  ▭
INK  ▭
OUT  ▭
END  ▭
```

4
```
PIT  ▭
PAT  ▭
PUT  ▭
PET  ▭
POT  ▭
```

5
```
OFF  ▭
DEW  ▭
DAY  ▭
HAT  ▭
BOW  ▭
```

6
```
OUT  ▭
ANT  ▭
END  ▭
ACT  ▭
AND  ▭
```

7
```
ACT  ▭
TEN  ▭
NET  ▭
AND  ▭
END  ▭
```

8
```
URN  ▭
ASK  ▭
ARK  ▭
IRK  ▭
SEE  ▭
```

9
```
ORE  ▭
OUR  ▭
ARE  ▭
AIR  ▭
EAR  ▭
```

10
```
CAR  ▭
OUR  ▭
PAN  ▭
HOT  ▭
HOW  ▭
```

How Did You Do?
Let's Find Out!

Here are the correct answers. You may mark your answers to these questions yourself. The three-letter word answer is on the left and the complete word, underlined, is on the right.

1   red   <u>SCORED</u>

2   ill   <u>GORILLAS</u>

3   ash   <u>SPLASHED</u>

4   pit   <u>HOSPITAL</u>

5   bow   <u>RAINBOW</u>

6   act   <u>PRACTICE</u>

7   end   <u>ATTENDED</u>

8   ask   <u>BASKET</u>

9   air   <u>STAIRCASE</u>

10   how   <u>SHOWER</u>

If you scored 7 or more out of 10

A great score, well done. Now move on to the next set of questions and see if you can continue your good work. Remember to look at the words you got wrong and make sure you understand why your answer was incorrect.

If you scored 4 to 6 out of 10

Read this advice below before moving on to the next set of questions.

⇨ Look at the answers. You should know all of these words. If you don't, try reading more often to improve your vocabulary. Also try the vocabulary builders on pages 92, 100 and 116, which aim to help you learn new words. You'll need to look up the words in a dictionary and practise using them in a sentence of your own.

⇨ Did you spell any words wrongly? For example, in question 4, some students think 'pet' or 'pat' could be used to make 'hospital', but that would make an incorrectly spelled word. If you find you're spelling fairly common words wrongly, spend more time practising your spelling.

If you scored fewer than 4 out of 10

These are difficult questions but you'll need to improve on this score. Read the suggestions below before moving on to the next set of questions.

⇨ Do you understand what you have to do? If not, ask an adult to read the instructions and go through the example with you again. Then take another look at your answers and see if you can correct them.

⇨ Remember the three-letter word must not be changed in any way. That is, you shouldn't need to move around the letters or change any of them. Also the three-letter word can be put into the word in CAPITALS in any position, including at the front or at the end.

⇨ If you don't recognise some of the words or you misspelled them, make sure you practise spelling common words. Also, make sure you read regularly at home.

⇨ Look at the vocabulary builders on pages 44, 60, 92, 100 and 116 to help you improve your vocabulary and spelling.

LESSON 2 PART 2

Now let's try some more. You have 10 minutes to complete this task, so work quickly. When you've finished ask an adult to mark it for you.

1 The pretty, green BOON floated into the sky.

2 The train went across the BGE over the river.

3 We were FHTENED when we saw the scary film.

4 She went to the post ICE to buy some stamps and post her letter.

5 When the TELEPH rang I answered it politely.

6 The car was towed to the GAE to be fixed.

7 On my birthday I had a DERFUL time.

8 I enjoyed DING my picture during art today.

9 The lovely HO had four enormous bedrooms.

10 After working for an hour on her homework, my sister felt TD.

LESSON 2 PART 2: ANSWER SHEET

Mark your answer by putting a horizontal line in one of the boxes, as in the example below.

Example:

END	☐
AND	⊟
ARE	☐
OUR	☐
ERE	☐

1

EEL	☐
ILL	☐
ALL	☐
OWL	☐
AIL	☐

2

OUR	☐
ROD	☐
RED	☐
RID	☐
ARE	☐

3

LIT	☐
RIG	☐
ARE	☐
ERR	☐
RUG	☐

4

LET	☐
OUT	☐
BAT	☐
BET	☐
OFF	☐

5

ANT	☐
OWN	☐
OWE	☐
ONE	☐
ODE	☐

6

RAG	☐
MAT	☐
RAT	☐
RIG	☐
ROD	☐

7

ONE	☐
WIN	☐
WON	☐
AND	☐
WAN	☐

8

ORE	☐
RAW	☐
RAN	☐
ERR	☐
OUR	☐

9

MET	☐
STY	☐
SET	☐
MEN	☐
USE	☐

10

HEN	☐
IRE	☐
ARE	☐
OUR	☐
RAN	☐

LESSON 3 Moving a Letter to Make Two New Words

In this exercise you'll begin with two words. The aim is to remove one letter from the first word and place it into the second word. When you've done this correctly, two new words will be made. Let's look at an example.

Example

brake   font

First look only at the word on the <u>left</u>. Now remove the first letter and see if it leaves a new word.

brake – taking off the 'b' leaves 'rake'

Great, that's a new word; now can you put the letter 'b' somewhere in the second word to make a new one? Let's try. You can make the following words:

bfont   fbont   fobnt   fonbt   fontb

None of these are real words so you'll have to go back to the word on the left and see if you can remove a different letter and still leave a new word. Now try again.

The next letter is 'r', and if you remove it you are left with 'bake'.

Great, 'bake' is also a word. Now try and put the letter 'r' into the word 'font'. You can make:

rfont   front   fornt   fonrt   fontr

The word 'front' is a real word. So you now know the letter you need to move is <u>r</u>.
That is the one you need to mark on your answer sheet.

HELPFUL HINTS

- It's important to work methodically. That means, do things in an orderly way and do it the same way each time. That way you'll get used to working out the answer!

- Start with the word on the left, and remember you'll need to make <u>two</u> new words.

- You can't use proper nouns or names as your answers to these questions. So even if you find a name such as 'Ken' you need to keep looking for the right answer.

LESSON 3 PART 1

Now look at the questions below. Try to do each one as quickly as you can and make sure you finish them all. When you've found the answer, mark it on the opposite page. When you've finished write down the time you took in the box at the top.

You have 10 minutes to complete this task, so work quickly!

1	stand	here
2	chart	tank
3	flick	rile
4	snack	sped
5	grime	step
6	flake	fees
7	coats	shut
8	chain	herd
9	clamp	late
10	blink	tale

LESSON 3 PART 1: ANSWER SHEET

Mark your answer by putting a horizontal line in one of the boxes, as in the example below.

Example:

1

2

3

4

5

6

7

8

9

10

How Did You Do? Let's Find Out!

Here are the correct answers. You may mark your answers to these questions yourself. The letter that is the correct answer is given on the left and the two new words are given on the right.

1   t   sand, there

2   h   cart, thank

3   f   lick, rifle

4   n   sack, spend

5   e   grim, steep

6   l   fake, flees or feels

7   o   cats, shout

8   a   chin, heard

9   p   clam, plate

10   b   link, table

If you scored 8 or more out of 10

This is great! Move on to the next set of questions and see if you can continue your good work. Aim to get a higher score if you got 8 or 9 this time.

If you scored 5 to 7 out of 10

Read this advice before moving on to the next set of questions.

⇨ Look at the answers. These are words you should know. If you don't then you'll need to start reading more to build your vocabulary. Also read vocabulary builders 3 and 4 (pages 92, 100 and 116), which help you learn new words. You'll need to look up the words in a dictionary and practise using them in sentences of your own.

⇨ Did you spell any of the words wrongly? For example, in question 2 some students think 'chart' should become 'hart', which is the correct spelling of another name for deer. However, where does the 'c' go? They think the second word should be 'tanck', but this is not a word. If you find you're spelling fairly common words wrongly, spend more time practising your spelling.

⇨ Remember that proper nouns do not count as answers on these tests. For example, in question 1, some students think that the 'd' should be removed from the first word to spell 'Stan'. But Stan is a person's name and so it shouldn't be used. Also, avoid thinking of names of products, for example Kellogg's, as these are also proper nouns. If you're not sure about proper nouns read more about them in *Practise & Pass 11 + Level One: Discover English*.

If you scored fewer than 5 out of 10

You need to work to improve on this score. Read the suggestions that follow before moving on to the next set of questions.

⇨ Do you understand what you have to do? If not, ask an adult to read the instructions and go through the example with you again. Then take another look at your answers and see if you can correct them. Remember, when you take the letter from the first word, it must leave a real word behind. The letter must then be placed somewhere in the second word to make another real word.

⇨ Remember that you aren't permitted to change the order of any of the other letters in order to make the new word.

⇨ If you don't recognise some of the words or you misspelled them, make sure you practise spelling common words. Also, read regularly at home to improve your spelling and vocabulary.

⇨ You should look at the vocabulary builders on pages 44, 60, 92, 100 and 116 as they will help you to improve your vocabulary and spelling.

LESSON 3 PART 2

My Time

My Score

Now look at the questions below; I've made these a little more difficult. You have 10 minutes to complete this task, so work quickly! Remember to ask an adult to mark this section for you.

1	plump	fight
2	crate	lock
3	tread	weigh
4	rider	gown
5	drain	bran
6	thing	lean
7	plain	nose
8	chink	lined
9	amble	clap
10	stale	boot

LESSON 3 PART 2: ANSWER SHEET

Mark your answer by putting a horizontal line in one of the boxes, as in the example below.

Example:

b ☐
r ▭
a ☐
k ☐
e ☐

1

p ☐
l ☐
u ☐
m ☐
p ☐

2

c ☐
r ☐
a ☐
t ☐
e ☐

3

t ☐
r ☐
e ☐
a ☐
d ☐

4

r ☐
i ☐
d ☐
e ☐
r ☐

5

d ☐
r ☐
a ☐
i ☐
n ☐

6

t ☐
h ☐
i ☐
n ☐
g ☐

7

p ☐
l ☐
a ☐
i ☐
n ☐

8

c ☐
h ☐
i ☐
n ☐
k ☐

9

a ☐
m ☐
b ☐
l ☐
e ☐

10

s ☐
t ☐
a ☐
l ☐
e ☐

LESSON 4 Using One Letter to Finish One Word and Start Another

In this exercise you'll need to find <u>one</u> letter to finish the word on the left and begin the word on the right so that two new words are formed. Here's an example.

Example

band   (?)   pout

Which letter will go on the end of band and the start of pout to make two new words?

The letter is <u>s</u> which makes bands and spout. This is the letter you should mark on your answer sheet.

HELPFUL HINTS

- Note that it's only one letter you need to find.

- You must make two new words and they must be real words. The new words cannot be proper nouns or names.

- If you can't work it out immediately, try going through the letters on the answer grid. You know that one of these will be the missing letter.

- Sometimes you might find a letter that works but it isn't on the answer grid. In that case you'll need to find a letter that works that is on the answer grid – sorry!

- If you get completely stuck, don't waste time – move on to the next question. Come back to the tricky questions at the end.

LESSON 4 PART 1

My Time

My Score

Now look at the questions below. When you've found the answer, mark it on the opposite page. Try to do each question as quickly as you can and make sure you complete them all. When you've finished, write down the time you took in the box at the top.

You have 10 minutes to complete this task, so work quickly.

1	past	(?)	very
2	spur	(?)	rain
3	card	(?)	wing
4	pin	(?)	not
5	pear	(?)	end
6	ski	(?)	ear
7	ten	(?)	rip
8	wit	(?)	eel
9	pal	(?)	arch
10	slum	(?)	luck

LESSON 4 PART 1: ANSWER SHEET

Mark your answer by putting a horizontal line in one of the boxes, as in the example below.

Example:

How Did You Do? Let's Find Out!

Here are the correct answers. You may mark your answers to these questions yourself. The letter that is the correct answer is given on the left side and the two new words that are formed are given underlined on the right side.

1   e   paste, every

2   t   spurt, train

3   s   cards, swing

4   k   pink, knot

5   l   pearl, lend

6   n   skin, near

7   d   tend, drip

8   h   with, heel

9   m   palm, march

10   p   slump, pluck

If you scored 8 or more out of 10

Well done – this is a great score. Make sure you check over the words you got wrong before moving on to the next test.

If you scored 5 to 7 out of 10

Take a look at the advice below before moving to the next set of questions.

⇨ Look at the answers. You should know all of these words. If you don't, you'll find it helpful to spend more time reading to help improve your vocabulary. Also, read the vocabulary builders on pages 92, 100 and 116, which help you learn new words. You'll need to look up the words in a dictionary and practise using them in a sentence of your own.

⇨ Did you spell any of the words wrongly? For example, in question 8, some students think the answer should be 's' to make wits and seel, but seel isn't a word. The correct spelling should be 'seal'. If you find you're spelling fairly common words wrongly, then you'll need to spend more time practising them. You can use the vocabulary builders on pages 44, 60, 92, 100 and 116 to help you with these.

If you scored fewer than 5 out of 10

This score needs to improve so read the suggestions that follow before moving on to the next set of questions.

⇨ Do you understand what you have to do? If not, ask an adult to read the instructions and go through the example with you again. Then take another look at your answers and see if you can correct them. Remember that you're looking for just <u>one</u> letter which will work for both words.

⇨ If you don't recognise some of the words or you misspelled them, make sure you practise spelling common words. Also try to read regularly at home.

⇨ Look at the vocabulary builders on pages 44, 60, 92, 100 and 116 to help you improve your vocabulary and spelling.

LESSON 4 PART 2

My Time

My Score

Now look at the questions below. Try to do each one as quickly as you can and make sure you finish them all. When you've found the right letter, mark it on the opposite page. Remember to ask an adult to mark these for you. When you've finished, write down the time you took and your score in the box at the top.

You have 10 minutes to complete this task, so work quickly.

1	win	(?)	host
2	glide	(?)	each
3	no	(?)	hen
4	weigh	(?)	rack
5	rot	(?)	mount
6	work	(?)	talk
7	store	(?)	ears
8	flow	(?)	eat
9	bee	(?)	lock
10	bat	(?)	eight

LESSON 4 PART 2: ANSWER SHEET

Mark your answer by putting a horizontal line in one of the boxes, as in the example below.

Example:

e ☐
s ▬
a ☐
y ☐
o ☐

1

s ☐
e ☐
y ☐
c ☐
g ☐

2

r ☐
p ☐
s ☐
t ☐
b ☐

3

b ☐
r ☐
w ☐
c ☐
d ☐

4

s ☐
c ☐
w ☐
t ☐
e ☐

5

s ☐
h ☐
e ☐
a ☐
y ☐

6

y ☐
s ☐
t ☐
e ☐
d ☐

7

y ☐
l ☐
m ☐
b ☐
p ☐

8

t ☐
n ☐
r ☐
d ☐
b ☐

9

t ☐
s ☐
r ☐
f ☐
n ☐

10

s ☐
e ☐
h ☐
w ☐
d ☐

LESSON 5 Completing Two Pairs of Words with the Same Letter

In this exercise, you'll need to work out which letter completes the first word and begins the second. The same letter must also be used to complete the second pair of incomplete words. Proper nouns cannot be used in this lesson.

Example

das (?) ard   las (?) ope

In this case the missing letter is 'h', which makes the words das<u>h</u>, <u>h</u>ard, las<u>h</u> and <u>h</u>ope. Although some other letters could be used to complete some of the words above, no other letter will work for all of them. So <u>h</u> is the letter you should mark on your answer sheet.

HELPFUL HINTS

- Four words must be made and they must all be real words.

- Note that it's only <u>one</u> letter that you'll need to find.

- If you can't find the right letter immediately, try going through the letters on the answer grid to help you find the missing letter.

- If you get completely stuck, don't waste time. Move on to the next question and come back to the tricky ones at the end.

LESSON 5 PART 1

My Time		My Score	

Now look at the questions below. Try to do each one as quickly as you can and make sure you finish them all. Once you've finished write your time and score in the boxes above.

You have 10 minutes to complete this task.

1	har	(?)	ace	cho	(?)	eat
2	vei	(?)	ape	sca	(?)	oun
3	tom	(?)	ell	thum	(?)	ark
4	sen	(?)	oll	war	(?)	ive
5	fis	(?)	alt	wit	(?)	ole
6	sic	(?)	een	too	(?)	nee
7	vist	(?)	ngle	iot	(?)	rrow
8	hos	(?)	ask	fre	(?)	rek
9	fle	(?)	are	cro	(?)	hip
10	los	(?)	alt	mes	(?)	ink

LESSON 5 PART 1: ANSWER SHEET

Mark your answer by putting a horizontal line in one of the boxes, as in the example below.

Example:

1	**2**	**3**	**4**

5	**6**	**7**	**8**

9	**10**

How Did You Do? Let's Find Out!

Here are the correct answers. You may mark your answers to these questions yourself. The correct letter is on the left and the four words it makes are given underlined on the right.

1   p   <u>harp</u>, <u>pace</u>, <u>chop</u>, <u>peat</u>

2   n   <u>vein</u>, <u>nape</u>, <u>scan</u>, <u>noun</u>

3   b   <u>tomb</u>, <u>bell</u>, <u>thumb</u>, <u>bark</u>

4   d   <u>send</u>, <u>doll</u>, <u>ward</u>, <u>dine</u>

5   h   <u>fish</u>, <u>halt</u>, <u>with</u>, <u>hole</u>

6   k   <u>sick</u>, <u>keen</u>, <u>took</u>, <u>knee</u>

7   a   <u>vista</u>, <u>angle</u>, <u>iota</u>, <u>arrow</u>

8   t   <u>host</u>, <u>task</u>, <u>fret</u>, <u>trek</u>

9   w   <u>flew</u>, <u>ware</u>, <u>crow</u>, <u>whip</u>

10   s   <u>loss</u>, <u>salt</u>, <u>mess</u>, <u>sink</u>

If you scored 7 or more out of 10

This is great! Move on to the next set of questions and see if you can continue your good work. But do look at the words you got wrong to help you improve for next time. I think these questions are tricky so you're doing really well!

If you scored 4 to 6 out of 10

Read this advice before moving on to the next set of questions.

⇨ Look at the answers. You should know all of these words. If you don't, you'll find it helpful to spend more time reading to improve your vocabulary. Also, read vocabulary builders 3 and 4 on pages 92, 100 and 116, which help you learn new words. You'll need to look up the words in a dictionary and practise using them in a sentence of your own.

⇨ Did you find a letter which worked with some words but not others? For example in question 9, some students think as the letter 'd' works to make 'fled' and 'dare' it should work for all the words; but 'crod' and 'dhip' show that it will not work for the second pair of words.

⇨ If you find you're spelling fairly common words wrongly, you'll need to spend more time practising them.

If you scored fewer than 4 out of 10

These are difficult questions but your score is going to have to improve. Read the suggestions that follow before moving on to the next set of questions.

⇨ Do you understand what you have to do? If not, ask an adult to read the instructions and go through the example with you. Then take another look at your answers and see if you can correct them. Remember that you're looking for just one letter that will work for all four words.

⇨ Look at the vocabulary builders on pages 44, 60, 92, 100 and 116 to help you improve your vocabulary and spelling.

LESSON 5 PART 2

My Time	My Score

Now look at the questions below. Try to do each one as quickly as you can but make sure you finish them all. You have 10 minutes to complete this task. Remember to ask an adult to mark these for you. Once you've finished, write your time and score in the boxes above.

1	plo	(?)	elp	cla	(?)	acht
2	spu	(?)	ice	tou	(?)	age
3	run	(?)	ift	fan	(?)	naw
4	lut	(?)	arl	gat	(?)	ver
5	pil	(?)	eaf	sea	(?)	ore
6	hee	(?)	own	see	(?)	aze
7	tur	(?)	ave	twi	(?)	ook
8	sla	(?)	ook	swa	(?)	ull
9	rif	(?)	own	fli	(?)	wig
10	lus	(?)	igh	loc	(?)	oot

LESSON 5 PART 2: ANSWER SHEET

Mark your answer by putting a horizontal line in one of the boxes, as in the example below.

Example:

VOCABULARY BUILDER 1
MISSING WORDS

Now it's time to build your vocabulary, that is, learn some more words. Choose words from the table below to fill in the blanks. They are all words that describe people's occupations. Use each word only once.

Make a note of which words end with 'er', 'or' and 'ar'; they sound similar but the different spellings can catch you out!

1 The _____ built a beautiful mansion.

2 The lucky _____ landed an enormous fish.

3 The child was sick so he had to see the _____.

4 The children listened carefully to their _____.

5 The person who writes a book is called the book's _____.

6 The _____ leads the country.

7 The _____ brought his boat safely into the harbour.

8 Before an article is printed it must be checked by an _____.

9 The brave _____ helped put out the fire in the house.

10 The medical _____ helped the doctor to treat the patient.

author	editor	sailor	builder	registrar
Prime Minister	angler	fire fighter	teacher	doctor

See page 126 for the answers.

REMEMBER – YOU WON'T FIND THIS KIND OF QUESTION IN THE TEST,
THIS IS HERE JUST TO GIVE YOU SOME EXTRA PRACTISE.

LESSON 6 Forming Compound Words

A compound word is a word that is formed when two or more words are joined together.

For example, when the words 'bed' and 'room' are joined together, they form a new word 'bedroom'.

In this exercise you're given two sets of three words. You'll need to choose one word from each set, which, when put together, will form one new word.

There are a couple of rules you need to remember when answering these questions: firstly, the word from the first set should always come first. Secondly, you mustn't add, remove or change the order of any letters in the words provided. Let's look at an example.

Example

ear	foot	shoulder
bat	club	ball

Work through the words methodically, starting with the words in the first set on the top row. For example, looking at the words above, you could start by trying to make a word beginning with 'ear'. You could make:

ear + bat =	earbat	But that's not a word!
ear + club =	earclub	But that's not a word!
ear + ball =	earball	But that's not a word!

So you need to move along to try the next word in the top row:

foot + bat =	footbat	But that's not a word!
foot + club =	footclub	But that's not a word!
foot + ball =	football	Now that is a word!

So you would mark the words <u>foot</u> and <u>ball</u> on your answer grid.

Remember, you must mark <u>both</u> words on your answer grid.

LESSON 6 PART 1

My Time	My Score

Now look at the questions below. Try to do each one as quickly as you can and make sure you finish them all. When you've found the correct pair of words mark both the words on the opposite page. When you've finished write down the time you took and your score in the boxes at the top.

You have 10 minutes to complete these, so work quickly!

1 thank   more   even
      full   less   me

2 in   out   big
      rage   there   small

3 up   all   down
      above   there   cast

4 this   in   my
      side   time   turn

5 metal   stair   police
      container station case

6 pine   toffee cooking
      table   pudding apple

7 pass   ship   harbour
      port   sea   side

8 her   them   we
      friend   will   self

9 hard   danger under
      us   ground time

10 old   dam   after
      time   age   that

LESSON 6 PART 1: ANSWER SHEET

Mark your answer by putting a horizontal line in one of the boxes in each column, as in the example below.

Example:

ear ☐	bat ☐
foot ▭	club ☐
shoulder ☐	ball ▭

1

thank ☐	full ☐
more ☐	less ☐
even ☐	me ☐

2

in ☐	rage ☐
out ☐	there ☐
big ☐	small ☐

3

up ☐	above ☐
all ☐	there ☐
down ☐	cast ☐

4

this ☐	side ☐
in ☐	time ☐
my ☐	turn ☐

5

metal ☐	container ☐
stair ☐	station ☐
police ☐	case ☐

6

pine ☐	table ☐
toffee ☐	pudding ☐
cooking ☐	apple ☐

7

pass ☐	port ☐
ship ☐	sea ☐
harbour ☐	side ☐

8

her ☐	friend ☐
them ☐	will ☐
we ☐	self ☐

9

hard ☐	us ☐
danger ☐	ground ☐
under ☐	time ☐

10

old ☐	time ☐
dam ☐	age ☐
after ☐	that ☐

How Did You Do? Let's Find Out!

Here are the correct answers. You may mark your answers to these questions yourself. The two words you should have chosen are on the left side and the compound word they make is given underlined on the right side.

1	thank	less	<u>thankless</u>
2	out	rage	<u>outrage</u>
3	down	cast	<u>downcast</u>
4	in	side	<u>inside</u>
5	stair	case	<u>staircase</u>
6	pine	apple	<u>pineapple</u>
7	pass	port	<u>passport</u>
8	her	self	<u>herself</u>
9	under	ground	<u>underground</u>
10	dam	age	<u>damage</u>

If you scored 7 or more out of 10

This is terrific! Read the further hint on the next page then move on to the next set of questions and see if you can continue your good work. But do look at the words you got wrong and make sure you understand why your answers were incorrect.

If you scored 4 to 7 out of 10

Read this advice and the further hint on the next page before moving on to the next set of questions.

⇨ Look at the words above. You should know them all. If you don't, you'll find it helpful to spend more time reading to help improve your vocabulary. Also, read the vocabulary builders on pages 44, 60, 92, 100 and 116, which help you learn new words.

⇨ Did you spell any of the words incorrectly? For example in question 1, some students think 'thank' should go with 'full' to make the word 'thankfull'. But this is an incorrect spelling, because 'thankful' is spelt with one 'l'. If you find you're spelling fairly common words incorrectly, you'll need to spend more time practising your spelling. Use the vocabulary builders to help you with this.

⇨ Did you put words together which made sense but didn't actually make one new compound word? For example in question 5, some students think 'police' and 'station' should go together to make 'police station'. However, this does not make <u>one</u> new word so it isn't correct. Be careful with these.

If you scored fewer than 4 out of 10

You're going to need to improve on this score. Below are some suggestions to help you, so read through them before moving on to the next set of questions.

⇨ Do you understand what you have to do? If not, ask an adult to read the instructions and go through the example with you again. Then take another look at your answers and see if you can correct them.

⇨ Remember that you shouldn't choose two words from the same set; you need to take a word from the first set and then choose one from the second set to make one new word.

⇨ If you don't recognise some of the words or you misspelled them, make sure you practise spelling common words. Also try to read regularly at home to improve your spelling.

⇨ Look at the vocabulary builders on pages 44, 60, 92, 100 and 116 to help you improve your vocabulary and spelling.

A further hint

When you're looking for two words which, when combined, create one new word remember that sometimes the pronunciation can change.

Example

fat + her = father

The words 'fat' and 'her' are pronounced completely differently when used to produce the word 'father'. Watch out for these, I may have put a few in the next set of questions!

LESSON 6 PART 2

My Time

My Score

Now let's try some more. You have 10 minutes to complete these, so work quickly! Mark your answers on the opposite page. Remember to ask an adult to mark these for you.

1   large   green   flat
     house   place   grass

2   more   bit   even
     less   ten   than

3   car   new   animal
     van   dog   pet

4   little   car   pend
     in   ant   and

5   mountain   high   cart
     lane   path   ridge

6   off   on   in
     stead   it   the

7   pass   old   new
     by   car   age

8   rat   mouse   see
     her   catcher   race

9   this   that   sea
     side   way   time

10   mist   back   before
     eerie   ward   then

LESSON 6 PART 2: ANSWER SHEET

Mark your answer by putting a horizontal line in one of the boxes in both sets of words for each answer, as in the example below.

Example:

ear	☐	bat	☐
foot	▭	club	☐
shoulder	☐	ball	▭

1

large	☐	house	☐
green	☐	place	☐
flat	☐	grass	☐

2

more	☐	less	☐
bit	☐	ten	☐
even	☐	than	☐

3

car	☐	van	☐
new	☐	dog	☐
animal	☐	pet	☐

4

little	☐	in	☐
car	☐	ant	☐
pend	☐	and	☐

5

mountain	☐	lane	☐
high	☐	path	☐
cart	☐	ridge	☐

6

off	☐	stead	☐
on	☐	it	☐
in	☐	the	☐

7

pass	☐	by	☐
old	☐	car	☐
new	☐	age	☐

8

rat	☐	her	☐
mouse	☐	catcher	☐
see	☐	race	☐

9

this	☐	side	☐
that	☐	way	☐
sea	☐	time	☐

10

mist	☐	eerie	☐
back	☐	ward	☐
before	☐	then	☐

LESSON 7 Finding Synonyms

A synonym is a word that has the same meaning as another word.

For example, the words 'quick' and 'fast' are synonyms.

In this exercise you're given two sets of words. You'll need to choose a word from each set which have the same meaning. You must always choose one word from the first set (on the top row), and one from the second set (the bottom row).

Example

dark	light	weight
heavy	black	faint

The answer to the example above should be <u>light</u> from the first set and <u>faint</u> from the second set.

Some students might think that 'dark' and 'black' would be the correct answers but these two words do not mean the same thing. Likewise, 'heavy' and 'weight' are related words but they do not have the same meaning. 'Light' and 'faint' do have the same meaning as they both mean something that might be hard to see.

HELPFUL HINTS

- Remember to choose one word from each set.

- Watch out for those tricky words that have more than one possible meaning. In the example above, 'light' could mean a light that you switch on to see better, or something that is the opposite of heavy, or something that is the opposite of dark.

- You must mark both words on your answer grid.

LESSON 7 PART 1

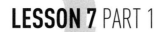

| My Time | My Score |

Now look at the questions below. Try to do each one as quickly as you can and make sure you finish them all. When you've found both words mark them on the opposite page. When you've finished write down the time you took and your score in the boxes at the top.

You have 10 minutes to complete these, so work quickly!

1   blast   explain   build
        return   calm   explode

2   discover   fumble   catch
        grope   retain   grip

3   hold   pitch   pouch
        football   sport   throw

4   shelve   revive   book
        achieve   postpone high

5   invisible lens   vision
        sight   narrow   light

6   trench   island   tunnel
        channel   coat   mound

7   hidden   sneak   brain
        creep   blunder   obvious

8   hide   know   reveal
        decide   revel   show

9   pardon   punish   reward
        penalise   agree   announce

10   moan   laugh   wing
        whinge   discuss   mourn

LESSON 7 PART 1: ANSWER SHEET

Mark your answer by putting a horizontal line in one of the boxes for both sets of words for each answer, as in the example below.

Example:

dark ▢	heavy ▢
light ▬	black ▢
weight ▢	faint ▬

1

blast ▢	return ▢
explain ▢	calm ▢
build ▢	explode ▢

2

discover ▢	grope ▢
fumble ▢	retain ▢
catch ▢	grip ▢

3

hold ▢	football ▢
pitch ▢	sport ▢
pouch ▢	throw ▢

4

shelve ▢	achieve ▢
revive ▢	postpone ▢
book ▢	high ▢

5

invisible ▢	sight ▢
lens ▢	narrow ▢
vision ▢	light ▢

6

trench ▢	channel ▢
island ▢	coat ▢
tunnel ▢	mound ▢

7

hidden ▢	creep ▢
sneak ▢	blunder ▢
brain ▢	obvious ▢

8

hide ▢	decide ▢
know ▢	revel ▢
reveal ▢	show ▢

9

pardon ▢	penalise ▢
punish ▢	agree ▢
reward ▢	announce ▢

10

moan ▢	whinge ▢
laugh ▢	discuss ▢
wing ▢	mourn ▢

How Did You Do?
Let's Find Out!

Here are the correct answers. You may mark your answers to these questions yourself. The two words from each set that you needed to mark on your answer sheet are listed.

1	blast	explode
2	fumble	grope
3	pitch	throw
4	shelve	postpone
5	vision	sight
6	trench	channel
7	sneak	creep
8	reveal	show
9	punish	penalise
10	moan	whinge

If you scored 7 or more out of 10

This is a good score – well done. Now move on to the next set of questions and aim for another great result by learning from any mistakes you made.

If you scored 4 to 7 out of 10

With a bit more work you'll be able to improve this score. Read this advice before moving on to the next set of questions.

Look at the answers. You should know all of these words. If you don't you'll find it useful to spend more time reading to help improve your vocabulary and you should try reading the vocabulary builders 3 and 4 (see pages 92, 100 and 116), to help you learn new words. You'll need to look up the words you learn in a dictionary and practise using them in a sentence of your own.

If you scored fewer than 4 out of 10

You'll need to work to improve your score. Read the suggestions that follow before moving on to the next set of questions.

⇨ Do you understand what you have to do? If not, ask an adult to read the instructions and go through the example with you again. Then take another look at your answers and see if you can correct them. Remember you must choose a word from the first set first and then choose one from the second set.

⇨ Remember that you shouldn't choose two words from the same set.

⇨ If you don't recognise some of the words or you don't fully understand their meaning make sure you look them up in a dictionary. Also try to read regularly at home, and work on your spelling.

⇨ Look at the vocabulary builders on pages 44, 60, 92, 100 and 116 to help you improve your vocabulary and spelling.

LESSON 7 PART 2

My Time	My Score

Now look at the questions below. Try to do each one as quickly as you can and make sure you finish them all. When you've found both words mark them on the opposite page. You have 10 minutes to complete these, so work quickly! When you've finished write down the time you took in the box at the top. Remember to ask an adult to mark these for you.

1
| level | rough | wavy |
| plain | plane | spiral |

2
| delay | drive | hurry |
| hasten | distance | hitch |

3
| breathe | gasp | shout |
| pant | grasp | sudden |

4
| swing | park | road |
| estate | extend | house |

5
| clear | awful | foggy |
| rainy | freezing | murky |

6
| find | escape | seek |
| dodge | fire | catch |

7
| donate | refuse | take |
| pledge | surprise | lose |

8
| play | break | count |
| down | win | record |

9
| buckle | release | shield |
| clasp | applause | belt |

10
| recent | evidence | ancient |
| different | olden | expensive |

LESSON 7 PART 2: ANSWER SHEET

Mark your answer by putting a horizontal line in one of the boxes for both sets of words for each answer, as in the example below.

Example:

dark ▢	heavy ▢
light ▬	black ▢
weight ▢	faint ▬

1

level ▢	plain ▢
rough ▢	plane ▢
wavy ▢	spiral ▢

2

delay ▢	hasten ▢
drive ▢	distance ▢
hurry ▢	hitch ▢

3

breathe ▢	pant ▢
gasp ▢	grasp ▢
shout ▢	sudden ▢

4

swing ▢	estate ▢
park ▢	extend ▢
road ▢	house ▢

5

clear ▢	rainy ▢
awful ▢	freezing ▢
foggy ▢	murky ▢

6

find ▢	dodge ▢
escape ▢	fire ▢
seek ▢	catch ▢

7

donate ▢	pledge ▢
refuse ▢	surprise ▢
take ▢	lose ▢

8

play ▢	down ▢
break ▢	win ▢
count ▢	record ▢

9

buckle ▢	clasp ▢
release ▢	applause ▢
shield ▢	belt ▢

10

recent ▢	different ▢
evidence ▢	olden ▢
ancient ▢	expensive ▢

VOCABULARY BUILDER 2
PROBLEMS TO SOLVE

Try to solve the problems below – remember to think of as many different words, and all of their different meanings, as you can.

1 Parts of the words in the list below all have something in common. Write what you think the link is on the line below.

_____

Can you add any words of your own to the list below? Write them in the spaces.

a) splash   1) _____

b) croak

c) helmet   2) _____

d) first

e) spine   3) _____

f) figure

g) steak   4) _____

2 Read the passage below and explain the order in which the animals can cross the river obeying all the rules.

'Two ducks (A and B) and a fox need to cross a river. There's a boat but only two animals can go in the boat at any one time. The fox must not be left with only one of the ducks anywhere since his appetite might get the better of him! The boat cannot move by itself.'

_____

_____

_____

_____

See page 126 for the answers.

REMEMBER – THESE ARE JUST FOR EXTRA PRACTISE!

LESSON 8 Finding the Two Wrongly Placed Words

In this exercise there are two words that are in the wrong place in each sentence. If these two words swap places the sentence will make sense.

You need to find both words and mark them in the answer grid. Let's look at an example.

Example

> Many chocolates like eating people.

In this example, clearly <u>chocolates</u> do not eat <u>people</u>! These two words should change places so that the sentence reads:

> Many people like eating chocolates.

So the two words to mark on the answer grid are: <u>people</u> and <u>chocolates</u>.

HELPFUL HINTS

- Read the sentence at normal speed. Find the first word that has been misplaced and underline it. Then think about where it should go – this should direct you to the second misplaced word. Underline this one too.

- Now read the sentence a final time with the words in the correct order. If it makes sense, mark these two words on your answer grid and move on. If the sentence still doesn't make sense try again.

- Make sure you mark <u>two</u> words for every question on your answer grid.

- Don't worry about whether a word has capital letters or not as this has no bearing on the correct answer.

LESSON 8 PART 1

My Time

My Score

Now look at the questions below. Try to do each one as quickly as you can and make sure you finish them all. Time yourself. You have 10 minutes to complete these. Some are quite tricky so if you get stuck, move on. Return to any difficult questions at the end.

1 Computer games are play to fun.

2 Hover birds can humming in mid air.

3 We could fire smoke from the see.

4 He went then exercised to bed early.

5 The tranquil looked very lagoon.

6 A before desert stood vast them.

7 A mobile digital can take phone pictures.

8 Their were three people walking there dogs this morning.

9 Submarines can under days spend the sea.

10 The path forest fires burned everything in their fierce.

LESSON 8 PART 1: ANSWER SHEET

Mark your answer by putting a horizontal line in two of the boxes, as in the example below.

Example:

many	☐
chocolates	⊟
like	☐
eating	☐
people	⊟

1

computer	☐
games	☐
are	☐
play	☐
fun	☐

2

hover	☐
birds	☐
can	☐
humming	☐
air	☐

3

could	☐
fire	☐
smoke	☐
from	☐
see	☐

4

went	☐
then	☐
exercised	☐
bed	☐
early	☐

5

the	☐
tranquil	☐
looked	☐
very	☐
lagoon	☐

6

before	☐
desert	☐
stood	☐
vast	☐
them	☐

7

take	☐
mobile	☐
digital	☐
phone	☐
pictures	☐

8

their	☐
three	☐
people	☐
there	☐
morning	☐

9

submarines	☐
under	☐
days	☐
spend	☐
sea	☐

10

path	☐
forest	☐
fires	☐
burned	☐
fierce	☐

⚙ How Did You Do?
Let's Find Out!

Here are the correct answers. You may mark your answers to these questions yourself. The two words which need to move in each sentence are given below.

1 play   fun

2 Hover   humming

3 fire   see

4 went   exercised

5 tranquil   lagoon

6 before   vast

7 digital   phone

8 Their   there

9 under   spend

10 path   fierce

If you scored 7 or more out of 10

This is great! Now move on to the next set of questions and see if you can continue your good work. But do look at any questions you got incorrect and try to learn any words you didn't know.

If you scored 4 to 6 out of 10

Read this advice before moving on to the next set of questions.

⇨ I consider these questions difficult so your score is still acceptable. To improve it you'll need to make sure the sentence makes sense when you swap both of the words.

⇨ The two words that need to be exchanged should become apparent to you on reading the sentence at normal speed.

If you scored fewer than 4 out of 10

Your score isn't great but these are difficult questions. Read the suggestions that follow before moving on to the next set of questions to improve for next time.

⇨ Do you understand what you have to do? If not, ask an adult to read the instructions and go through the example with you again. Then take another look at your answers and see if you can correct them. Remember you must find the <u>two</u> words that change places for the sentence to make sense, not just one.

⇨ The two words must change places with <u>each other</u>, they cannot be placed somewhere else in the sentence.

LESSON 8 PART 2

My Time	My Score

Now have a look at the questions below. They're slightly more complicated so you'll really need to be careful. You have 10 minutes again so try your best and keep going right to the end.

Remember to ask an adult to mark these for you.

1 The well footballer played amazing.

2 I friends and my love painting pictures.

3 The round cars sped two the track.

4 The fire dragon breathed fearsome on its enemies.

5 The sirens on blared ambulance the loudly.

6 We could hear lightning and see thunder.

7 The explorer carefully his studied map.

8 The precariously hovered helicopter before landing.

9 Dwelled down in the dark cave deep a monster.

10 'Its alive,' said the scientist, 'You can tell by it's breathing.'

LESSON 8 PART 2: ANSWER SHEET

Mark your answer by putting a horizontal line in two of the boxes, as in the example below.

Example:

many	☐
chocolates	▬
like	☐
eating	☐
people	▬

1

The	☐
well	☐
footballer	☐
played	☐
amazing	☐

2

I	☐
friends	☐
my	☐
love	☐
painting	☐

3

round	☐
cars	☐
sped	☐
two	☐
track	☐

4

fire	☐
dragon	☐
breathed	☐
fearsome	☐
enemies	☐

5

sirens	☐
blared	☐
ambulance	☐
the	☐
loudly	☐

6

could	☐
hear	☐
lightning	☐
see	☐
thunder	☐

7

explorer	☐
carefully	☐
his	☐
map	☐
studied	☐

8

precariously	☐
hovered	☐
helicopter	☐
before	☐
landing	☐

9

dwelled	☐
down	☐
dark	☐
cave	☐
deep	☐

10

Its	☐
alive	☐
scientist	☐
it's	☐
breathing	☐

LESSON 9 Working Out the Missing Letters for Each Sequence

In this exercise, you'll use the alphabet to help you work out the missing letters that complete each sequence. Let's move straight to some examples.

A B C D E F G H I J K L M N O P Q R S T U V W X Y Z

Example 1

> A   E   I   M   _

In the example above, using the alphabet, you can see that there are three letters between each of the letters in the sequence, or four 'jumps' to reach each of the following letters. This means the next letter in the sequence is '<u>Q</u>'.

Example 2

> BZ   DX   FV   HT   _

In the example above it's easiest to look first at the first letter of each pair alone. If you look at the alphabet and track the letters you can see that there are two jumps from B to D, then another two jumps from D to F, and another two from F to H. If you continue this sequence with a further two jumps you'll arrive at 'J'.

Now you can tackle the second letter of each pair. They go Z, X, V, T. In this case, you can see that from Z to X you'll need to make two jumps backwards. This sequence continues for X to V and V to T. If you continue it once more you'll arrive at 'R'. Using these two sequences you get the final answer '<u>JR</u>'.

HELPFUL HINTS

- For all questions of this nature, you'll be provided with the full alphabet at the top of the page. Make sure you use it!

- There are many different letter patterns, so use a pencil to draw on your alphabet. The pattern for each will then become clear and you will see what the next letter should be. Then erase your lines and move on to the next question.

- When pairs of letters are used, sometimes you'll need to look at the first letter of each pair alone and then the second (see example 2 above).

- If you find that you get to the end of the alphabet but still need to make more jumps, just go back to the beginning of the alphabet and continue to count along your letters until you get to the correct one.

LESSON 9 PART 1

My Time

My Score

Now look at the questions below. Use the alphabet at the top of the list of questions to help you. Complete as many questions as you can as quickly as possible. You have 10 minutes to complete this task, so work quickly.

The blank lines at the end of each series simply show where the letters are missing. But you must mark your answer on the grid on the opposite page.

A B C D E F G H I J K L M N O P Q R S T U V W X Y Z

1 A	E	I	O	_____
2 B	C	E	H	_____
3 LO	JQ	HS	FU	_____
4 H	I	G	J	_____
5 B	Y	E	V	_____
6 G	F	D	A	_____
7 S	R	T	Q	_____
8 RI	PK	NM	LO	_____
9 EFG	KLM	QRS	WXY	_____
10 GJ	JM	MP	PS	_____

LESSON 9 PART 1: ANSWER SHEET

Mark your answer by putting a horizontal line in one of the boxes as in the examples below.

Example 1:

```
L  ☐
O  ☐
P  ☐
Q  ▬
R  ☐
```

Example 2:

```
JR  ▬
IQ  ☐
LO  ☐
NN  ☐
IU  ☐
```

1

```
L  ☐
M  ☐
S  ☐
T  ☐
U  ☐
```

2

```
F  ☐
I  ☐
K  ☐
L  ☐
M  ☐
```

3

```
AJ  ☐
BK  ☐
CL  ☐
DW  ☐
EN  ☐
```

4

```
F  ☐
K  ☐
E  ☐
L  ☐
D  ☐
```

5

```
S  ☐
P  ☐
M  ☐
J  ☐
H  ☐
```

6

```
E  ☐
X  ☐
W  ☐
V  ☐
D  ☐
```

7

```
W  ☐
O  ☐
V  ☐
P  ☐
U  ☐
```

8

```
KP  ☐
JQ  ☐
IR  ☐
HS  ☐
GT  ☐
```

9

```
XYZ  ☐
ZAB  ☐
ABC  ☐
BCD  ☐
CDE  ☐
```

10

```
ST  ☐
SU  ☐
SV  ☐
SW  ☐
SX  ☐
```

71

How Did You Do? Let's Find Out!

Here are the correct answers. You may mark your answers to these questions yourself.

1 U

2 L

3 DW

4 F

5 H

6 W

7 U

8 JQ

9 CDE

10 SV

If you scored 8 or more out of 10

This is a great result, now move on to the next set of questions and see if you can continue your good work, but do check over any questions you got incorrect so you can improve for next time.

If you scored 5 to 7 out of 10

I consider these questions quite difficult, so your score is still acceptable. But to improve it you'll need to use the alphabet carefully to help work out each pattern. See the helpful hints on page 69 to help you with this.

If you scored fewer than 5 out of 10

These are difficult questions but your score needs to be better. Read the suggestions that follow before moving on to the next set of questions.

⇨ Do you understand what you have to do? If not, ask an adult to read the instructions and go through the examples with you again. Try to fully understand where you went wrong.

⇨ Remember to take care and use the alphabet provided at the top of the page – it's there to help you

LESSON 9 PART 2

Now let's try some more. This type of question is quite common so the more practice you can get, the better! You have 10 minutes again. Remember to mark your answer on the answer grid after you've worked it out.

A B C D E F G H I J K L M N O P Q R S T U V W X Y Z

1	Q	L	H	E	_____
2	F	J	K	O	_____
3	JK	IL	HM	GN	_____
4	Q	R	P	Q	_____
5	W	V	T	P	_____
6	H	I	L	Q	_____
7	N	M	O	L	_____
8	D	W	G	T	_____
9	BAZ	DDD	FGH	HJL	_____
10	P	R	Q	S	_____

LESSON 9 PART 2: ANSWER SHEET

Mark your answer by putting a horizontal line in one of the boxes, as in the examples below.

Example 1:

```
L ☐
O ☐
P ☐
Q ▤
R ☐
```

Example 2:

```
JR ▤
IQ ☐
LO ☐
NN ☐
IU ☐
```

1

```
D ☐
C ☐
B ☐
A ☐
Z ☐
```

2

```
P ☐
Q ☐
R ☐
S ☐
T ☐
```

3

```
GO ☐
FN ☐
FO ☐
EP ☐
FP ☐
```

4

```
P ☐
O ☐
N ☐
M ☐
L ☐
```

5

```
O ☐
N ☐
L ☐
K ☐
H ☐
```

6

```
R ☐
T ☐
V ☐
X ☐
Z ☐
```

7

```
P ☐
K ☐
Q ☐
J ☐
R ☐
```

8

```
I ☐
R ☐
J ☐
Q ☐
K ☐
```

9

```
IKO ☐
JLP ☐
JMP ☐
LMP ☐
MOQ ☐
```

10

```
Q ☐
R ☐
S ☐
T ☐
U ☐
```

LESSON 10 Working Out Direct Codes for Words

In this exercise, you're given one word and told what the code is for each of its letters.

A code is a piece of information (in this case letters) which is used to represent other information.

So in these questions you are told that certain letters represent other letters, and using this information you'll have to either find what word a code stands for, or turn a word into code.

Example 1

The code C V W L T D stands for S Q U A R E.

What is the code for A Q U A?

First write the code letters above the word like this:

C V W L T D

S Q U A R E

Now assign the letters:

S = C, Q = V, U = W, A = L, R = T, E = D

So you can see that the code for A Q U A is <u>L V W L</u>.

Example 2

Using the same code as above, what does the code DTLCD stand for?

Again you can assign letters like this:

D = E, T = R, L = A, C = S, D = E

So D T L C D stands for <u>ERASE</u>.

HELPFUL HINT

Write the code letters directly above the word you're given; that way it's easier to work out the codes of the other words that follow.

LESSON 10 PART 1

My Time

My Score

Now look at the questions below. Complete as many questions as you can. You have 10 minutes to complete this task, so work quickly and carefully.

A The code B L T M X V G J stands for S P O R A D I C.

How do you write:

1 RAPID

2 CORRIDOR

3 PAIR

What do these codes mean?

4 BTXL

5 BJXM

6 MXVGT

B The code D V R X B H C Y Z Q stands for G E L A T I N O U S.

How do you write:

7 ANGLE

8 TINGLE

9 STALE

10 GLINT

LESSON 10 PART 1: ANSWER SHEET

Mark your answer by putting a horizontal line in one of the boxes, as in the examples below.

Example 1:

LVWL ▬
LWVL ▭
WLVL ▭
VLWL ▭
WLVV ▭

Example 2:

RARER ▭
ERASE ▬
EASES ▭
SEERS ▭
ERROR ▭

1
MLXGV ▭
MLXVG ▭
MXLGV ▭
MXLVG ▭
MXLVV ▭

2
JTMMVGTM ▭
JTMMTVGM ▭
JTMMVMGT ▭
JTMMVTGM ▭
JTMMGVTM ▭

3
LXGM ▭
LGXM ▭
LMXG ▭
LXMG ▭
LMGX ▭

4
SPAR ▭
PORE ▭
SORE ▭
SOAP ▭
SEEP ▭

5
SLIP ▭
SLOP ▭
SCAR ▭
SOAR ▭
SAIL ▭

6
RAIDS ▭
DARES ▭
ROARS ▭
RADIO ▭
DOORS ▭

7
XCDVR ▭
XCVDR ▭
XCRDV ▭
XCVRD ▭
XCDRV ▭

8
BHCDRV ▭
BHCVDR ▭
BHCRDV ▭
BHCVRD ▭
BHCRVD ▭

9
QBVRX ▭
QBRXV ▭
QBXVR ▭
QBXRV ▭
QBVXR ▭

10
DRCHB ▭
DRBCH ▭
DRBHC ▭
DRHCB ▭
DRHBC ▭

How Did You Do?
Let's Find Out!

Here are the correct answers. You may mark your answers to these questions yourself.

1 MXLGV

2 JTMMGVTM

3 LXGM

4 SOAP

5 SCAR

6 RADIO

7 XCDRV

8 BHCDRV

9 QBXRV

10 DRHCB

If you scored 8 or more out of 10

This is great! Move on to the next set of questions and see if you can continue your good work but do check over any questions you got incorrect.

If you scored 5 to 7 out of 10

I consider these questions fairly straightforward so you need to work to improve your score. Make sure that you figure out the codes carefully by placing the word clue directly above or below the code. In this way you can work out the answer.

If you scored fewer than 5 out of 10

These aren't the most difficult questions you'll face so your score needs to improve. Read the suggestions that follow before moving on to the next set of questions.

⇨ Do you understand what you have to do? If not, ask an adult to read the instructions and go through the example with you again.

⇨ Make sure you work out the codes carefully.

⇨ Make sure your writing is neat and tidy so as to avoid unnecessary mistakes.

LESSON 10 PART 2

My Time

My Score

Now let's try some more. You have another 10 minutes to complete this task. Remember to ask an adult to mark them for you once you've finished.

A   The secret code D V R X B H C Y Z Q stands for G E L A T I N O U S.

What do these codes mean?

1 QRHCD

2 DXBV

3 QHCDRV

4 VCRHQB

B   The secret code G I H O J S M stands for C A R E F U L.

How do you write:

5 FUEL

6 FLARE

7 LEAF

What do these codes mean?

8 GIMMOH

9 JOIH

10 GIHOH

LESSON 10 PART 2: ANSWER SHEET

Mark your answer by putting a horizontal line in one of the boxes, as in the examples below.

Example 1:

LVWL	▭
LWVL	▭
WLVL	▭
VLWL	▭
WLVV	▭

Example 2:

RARER	▭
ERASE	▭
EASES	▭
SEERS	▭
ERROR	▭

1

NAILS	▭
SINGS	▭
GAINS	▭
SAILS	▭
SLING	▭

2

GALE	▭
GATE	▭
LATE	▭
GOAL	▭
GOAT	▭

3

TINGLE	▭
GLINTS	▭
STINGS	▭
SLINGS	▭
SINGLE	▭

4

ENLIST	▭
LISTEN	▭
TINSEL	▭
SENILE	▭
TITLES	▭

5

JMOS	▭
JOSM	▭
JOMS	▭
JSOM	▭
JMSO	▭

6

JMHIO	▭
JMIHO	▭
JMOHI	▭
JMHOI	▭
JMIOH	▭

7

MJOI	▭
MOIJ	▭
MOJI	▭
MIJO	▭
MIOJ	▭

8

RECALL	▭
CLEARS	▭
CALLER	▭
FACETS	▭
SCARES	▭

9

FREE	▭
FARE	▭
REEF	▭
RIFE	▭
FEAR	▭

10

RACER	▭
CARER	▭
RARER	▭
CLEAR	▭
FLARE	▭

LESSON 11 Working Out Indirect Codes for Words

In this exercise, you're given one word and the code for it. You'll then need to apply this same code to another word. Remember that these questions are different from the questions in lesson 10. Here, each question provides a new code, whereas in lesson 10 you could use one code for several questions.

These questions can have different forms. Let's look at some examples.

A B C D E F G H I J K L M N O P Q R S T U V W X Y Z

1   The word and code have the same number of letters:

Example 1

If LION = MGRJ, how do you write PARK?

In this example, by looking at the alphabet, you can see that M is one jump forward from L; G is two jumps back from I, R is three jumps forward from O and J is four jumps back from N. If you apply this code to PARK it is written as <u>QUYG</u>.

2   Sometimes a word might be hidden among other letters:

Example 2

If LFAGNHDI means LAND, how do you write MILK?

In this case, the word LAND is hidden among the letters FGHI. If you replace the letters of LAND with the letters of MILK the new code is <u>MFIGLHKI</u>.

3   Sometimes numbers are used. Often these refer to the corresponding letter of the alphabet, for example A = 1, B = 2, but not always!

Example 3

If 2 5 12 20 means BELT, what does 6 9 19 8 mean?

Since the numbers represent where each letter comes in the alphabet, 6 9 19 8 means <u>FISH</u>.

HELPFUL HINTS

- Count how many jumps there are between each letter and its code.

- Check each letter in the word as the code could be different for each one.

- Remember to use the alphabet at the top of the page to help you.

LESSON 11 PART 1

My Time

My Score

Now look at the questions below. Try to do them as quickly as possible. Move on if you find a particular question tricky. You can always come back to it. You have 10 minutes to complete this task.

A B C D E F G H I J K L M N O P Q R S T U V W X Y Z

1 If BITE is written as DKVG, how would you write CRAB?

2 If DILT means GLOW, what does YBKA mean?

3 If PURE is written as RYXM, how would you write DIVE?

4 If KYKZ means LAND, what does SYKG mean?

5 If PART is written as TRAP, how would you write STAR?

6 If SLIP is written as SXLYIZP what does JXUYMZP mean?

7 If 8 1 18 16 means HARP, what does 13 5 14 4 mean?

8 If CAT is written CAABTC, how will you write DOG?

9 If FLLAGG means FLAG, what does SHHOPP mean?

10 If YRT means BIG, what does QZN mean?

LESSON 11 PART 1: ANSWER SHEET

Mark your answer by putting a horizontal line in one of the boxes as in the examples below.

Example 1:

QUYG	▬
PTXF	☐
QWYG	☐
QUYF	☐
QUXG	☐

Example 2:

FMGIHLIK	☐
MFIGLHKI	▬
MIFGLHKI	☐
MIIHLGKF	☐
MFILGHKI	☐

Example 3:

GASH	☐
LASH	☐
FISH	▬
WISH	☐
DISH	☐

1

BTCD	☐
CTCD	☐
DTCD	☐
ETCD	☐
FTCD	☐

2

FEND	☐
LEND	☐
BENT	☐
LENT	☐
BEND	☐

3

FMBM	☐
GMBM	☐
FNBM	☐
FMBN	☐
FMCM	☐

4

TALK	☐
TANS	☐
SANK	☐
RANK	☐
TANK	☐

5

PATS	☐
RATS	☐
OATS	☐
PETS	☐
SETS	☐

6

PUNY	☐
JURY	☐
DUMP	☐
JUMP	☐
PUMP	☐

7

LEND	☐
MEND	☐
PEND	☐
SEND	☐
TEND	☐

8

DBOBGC	☐
CAOBGC	☐
DABOGC	☐
DOABGC	☐
DAOBGC	☐

9

HOPS	☐
POSH	☐
HOOP	☐
SHOP	☐
HOPE	☐

10

JAR	☐
MAP	☐
RAP	☐
JOB	☐
JAM	☐

How Did You Do? Let's Find Out!

Here are the correct answers. You may mark your answers to these questions yourself.

1 ETCD

2 BEND

3 FMBM

4 TANK

5 RATS

6 JUMP

7 MEND

8 DAOBGC

9 SHOP

10 JAM

If you scored 7 or more out of 10

Well done! Move on to the next set of questions but do check over any questions you got incorrect to help you do better next time.

If you scored 4 to 6 out of 10

I consider these questions quite tough so your score isn't terrible but you will need to improve it. To do this, make sure that you figure out the codes carefully by checking the letters or numbers, checking the sequences carefully, or looking to see if one word is placed inside other letters.

If you scored fewer than 4 out of 10

This is a low score. Read the suggestions that follow before moving on to the next set of questions.

⇨ Do you understand what you have to do? If not, ask an adult to read the instructions and go through the examples with you again.

⇨ Make sure you work out the codes carefully and write neatly to avoid any unnecessary mistakes.

LESSON 11 PART 2

My Time

My Score

Now let's try some more and see if we can speed up! You have 10 minutes again, so try to spot the code quickly and figure out the correct answer. Remember to mark your answer on the answer grid – and that an adult needs to mark these for you.

A B C D E F G H I J K L M N O P Q R S T U V W X Y Z

1 If BEAN is written as 2 F 1 O, how would you write SAFE?

2 If R 15 T 16 means SOUP, what does B 1 J 5 mean?

3 If STOP means POTS, what does DOOM mean?

4 If GRAPH is written as HTDTM, how would you write FLEET?

5 If HEN is written as KHQ, how would you write DAB?

6 If GONE is written as HNOD, how would you write BAND?

7 If BALL is written as CCOP, how would you write FOOT?

8 If CONE is written as 3 15 14 5, how would you write RAGS?

9 If SAD is written as SAABDC, how would you write HAPPY?

10 If MAKE is written as NYNA, how would you write BOAT?

LESSON 11 PART 2: ANSWER SHEET

Mark your answer by putting a horizontal line in one of the boxes, as in the examples below.

Example 1:

QUYG	▬
PTXF	☐
QWYG	☐
QUYF	☐
QUXG	☐

Example 2:

FMGIHLIK	☐
MFIGLHKI	▬
MIFGLHKI	☐
MIIHLGKF	☐
MFILGHKI	☐

Example 3:

GASH	☐
LASH	☐
FISH	▬
WISH	☐
DISH	☐

1

20 C 7 E	☐
19 C 7 E	☐
20 B 6 F	☐
19 B 6 F	☐
19 D 6 E	☐

2

CANE	☐
BAKE	☐
CAKE	☐
BEAN	☐
BEAT	☐

3

MODE	☐
DOME	☐
DEEM	☐
MADE	☐
MOOD	☐

4

GMHIY	☐
GNHIY	☐
FMHIY	☐
FNHIY	☐
GNHIX	☐

5

FDE	☐
GDF	☐
GEF	☐
GDE	☐
FDG	☐

6

DZAC	☐
CZAC	☐
DZOC	☐
EZOC	☐
CZOC	☐

7

GQPY	☐
GQPX	☐
GQRY	☐
GQRX	☐
GQRZ	☐

8

17 2 8 20	☐
19 2 6 18	☐
18 2 7 19	☐
18 1 7 19	☐
18 3 7 19	☐

9

HAABPCPDYE	☐
HAPBCDPYE	☐
HABPCPDYE	☐
HAAPBPCYD	☐
HAABPCYDE	☐

10

DMDP	☐
CMEP	☐
CNDP	☐
CMDP	☐
CMEE	☐

VOCABULARY BUILDER 3
SYNONYMS AND ANTONYMS (A)

Complete the table below using a dictionary or a thesaurus. This is a great way to expand your vocabulary.

Starter word	Words with similar meaning (synonym)			Word with opposite meaning (antonym)
	Word 1	Word 2	Word 3	
tiny				
enormous				
dreadful				
beautiful				
loud				
strange				
talk				
walk				
quickly				
carefully				

Now try to use some of your new words in simple sentences. That way you'll remember their meaning and understand how they are used.

1 _____

2 _____

3 _____

4 _____

5 _____

REMEMBER – THIS IS JUST EXTRA PRACTISE!

LESSON 12 Completing Number Patterns

In the next two lessons you'll be using numbers. You may think that this is mathematics and not verbal reasoning, but numerical-style questions can turn up on a verbal reasoning test. You might find that questions similar to these appear on a maths test too, so it's well worth practising them.

For these questions look at the list of numbers provided to work out what the pattern is and decide which number should come next.

Example 1

| 2 | 4 | 6 | 8 | _____ |

In this example, you can see that the numbers increase by 2 each time. Therefore the next number is <u>10</u>.

Example 2

| 12 | 72 | 18 | 66 | 24 | _____ |

In this example, you'll need to skip a number each time as there are two different patterns. The first pattern goes from 12 to 18 to 24 – increasing by 6 each time. The second pattern goes from 72 to 66 to '<u>60</u>', which will be your answer. This pattern decreases by 6 each time. Watch out for questions which use two different patterns.

Example 3

| 346 | 455 | 564 | _____ |

In this example you'll need to look at each digit individually. So you can see the first digit in each number increases by one each time as does the second, but the third digit decreases by 1 each time. So the answer is <u>673</u>.

HELPFUL HINTS

- Look for patterns of addition, subtraction, multiplication and division first.

- Watch out for set patterns, such as prime, square or cube numbers.

- A **prime number** can only be divided exactly by itself and the number 1. The first prime number and the only even one is the number 2.

- A **square number** is formed when a number is multiplied by itself. For example 7 × 7 = 49 so 49 is a square number.

- A **cube number** is formed when a number is multiplied by itself and that answer is then multiplied once more by the original number. For example 3 × 3 = 9 and 3 × 9 = 27 so 27 is a cube number formed by 3 × 3 × 3.

LESSON 12 PART 1

My Time

My Score

Now look at the questions below. Work out which number should come next in each pattern. Remember to mark your answer on the opposite page – don't write it on the blank line. Work quickly – you've 10 minutes to complete this task.

1	7	14	21	28	35	_____
2	6	9	12	15	18	_____
3	27	23	19	15	11	_____
4	12	13	18	19	24	_____
5	3	6	12	24	48	_____
6	243	81	27	9	3	_____
7	13	17	23	12	33	_____
8	248	357	466	575	684	_____
9	2.3	2.9	3.5	4.1	4.7	_____
10	2	5	7	12	19	_____

LESSON 12 PART 1: ANSWER SHEET

Mark your answer by putting a horizontal line in one of the boxes, as in the examples below.

Example 1:

8	☐
9	☐
10	▬
11	☐
12	☐

Example 2:

30	☐
60	▬
36	☐
54	☐
42	☐

Example 3:

663	☐
573	☐
673	▬
674	☐
574	☐

1

40	☐
41	☐
42	☐
43	☐
44	☐

2

20	☐
21	☐
22	☐
23	☐
24	☐

3

9	☐
8	☐
7	☐
6	☐
5	☐

4

25	☐
26	☐
27	☐
30	☐
31	☐

5

51	☐
54	☐
72	☐
96	☐
100	☐

6

3	☐
2	☐
1	☐
0	☐
−3	☐

7

43	☐
53	☐
54	☐
21	☐
7	☐

8

683	☐
693	☐
794	☐
793	☐
783	☐

9

5.0	☐
5.1	☐
5.2	☐
5.3	☐
5.4	☐

10

24	☐
26	☐
28	☐
30	☐
31	☐

How Did You Do?
Let's Find Out!

Here are the correct answers. You may mark your answers to these questions yourself.

1	42
2	21
3	7
4	25
5	96
6	1
7	7
8	793
9	5.3
10	31

If you scored 8 or more out of 10

A good result, well done! Move on to the next set of questions and see if you can continue your good work. But do check over any questions that you got incorrect.

If you scored 5 to 7 out of 10

I consider these questions relatively straightforward, so you'll need to improve your score. Make sure you know your multiplication tables by heart – this will help you speed up on these questions.

If you scored fewer than 5 out of 10

Fewer than 4 is a low score so you need to work hard to improve for the next set of questions. Read the suggestions that follow before moving on.

⇨ Do you understand what you have to do? If not, ask an adult to read the instructions and go through the examples with you again.

⇨ Make sure you work out the pattern by using your knowledge of addition, subtraction, multiplication and division.

⇨ Look out for other types of questions, such as two different patterns in one (where some numbers are skipped) or where you need to look at the individual digits to work out the pattern.

⇨ Make sure you can recognise set patterns such as prime, square and cube numbers.

LESSON 12 PART 2

| My Time | My Score |

Now look at the questions below. Try to work out which number should come next in each pattern. Remember to mark your answer on the opposite page. Don't write on the blank lines below. Work quickly – you have 10 minutes. Watch out for any set patterns of numbers which you should recognise quickly – I may have put some in this time! Ask an adult to mark this set for you.

#					
1	63	54	45	36	27	_____
2	7	10	20	23	43	_____
3	64	52	40	28	16	_____
4	1	2	2	4	8	_____
5	2	3	5	7	11	_____
6	27	6	24	9	21	_____
7	835	745	655	565	475	_____
8	19.3	18.2	17.1	16	14.9	_____
9	4	9	16	25	36	_____
10	17	20	19	22	21	_____

LESSON 12 PART 2: ANSWER SHEET

Mark your answer by putting a horizontal line in one of the boxes, as in the examples, below.

Example 1:

8	☐
9	☐
10	⊟
11	☐
12	☐

Example 2:

30	☐
60	⊟
36	☐
54	☐
42	☐

Example 3:

663	☐
573	☐
673	⊟
674	☐
574	☐

1

20	☐
19	☐
18	☐
17	☐
16	☐

2

46	☐
92	☐
69	☐
72	☐
43	☐

3

6	☐
5	☐
4	☐
3	☐
2	☐

4

8	☐
12	☐
16	☐
32	☐
64	☐

5

12	☐
13	☐
14	☐
15	☐
16	☐

6

18	☐
16	☐
15	☐
12	☐
11	☐

7

485	☐
386	☐
376	☐
375	☐
385	☐

8

13.9	☐
13.8	☐
13.7	☐
13.6	☐
13.5	☐

9

47	☐
61	☐
49	☐
41	☐
59	☐

10

24	☐
23	☐
22	☐
21	☐
20	☐

VOCABULARY BUILDER 3
SYNONYMS AND ANTONYMS (B)

Here's a blank table that you can fill in with some words that you've learned as you've worked through the book.

Starter word	Words with similar meaning (synonym)			Word with opposite meaning (antonym)
	Word 1	Word 2	Word 3	

Now try to use some of your new words in simple sentences.

1 _____

2 _____

3 _____

4 _____

5 _____

REMEMBER – THIS IS JUST FOR EXTRA PRACTISE!

LESSON 13 Replacing Letters with Numbers to Solve an Equation

In this exercise each letter is assigned a number. An equation is then written using the letters. You'll need to replace the letters with their corresponding numbers and work out the equation to choose the correct letter for your answer. Mark this letter on your answer grid.

Does it sound confusing? Don't worry, they're pretty simple once you've tried a few. Let's look at an example.

Example

If A = 2, B = 3, C = 4, D = 5 and E = 6, what is the answer to:

$$A \times B + E - C - D?$$

First you should write the numbers using the simple code given above:

$$2 \times 3 + 6 - 4 - 5$$

Now you can work this out:

$$2 \times 3 = 6; \quad 6 + 6 = 12; \quad 12 - 4 = 8; \quad 8 - 5 = 3$$

The letter that represents 3 is <u>B</u> so that is the letter that you should mark on your answer grid.

HELPFUL HINTS

- The code changes for each question so watch out for this.

- Remember that when you've found your answer you must convert it back to a letter (using the same code), and mark that on the answer grid.

- Work the problems out quickly on a piece of rough working paper so you don't have to remember too much at one time.

LESSON 13 PART 1

My Time

My Score

Now look at the questions below. Work out the sum and remember to mark your answer on the answer grid on the opposite page. Work quickly. You have 10 minutes to complete this task.

1 If A = 1, B = 2, C = 3, D = 4 and E = 5, what is the answer to: $(B + C) \times D \div E?$

2 If A = 2, B = 3, C = 4, D = 5 and E = 15, what is the answer to: $A \times B + C + D?$

3 If A = 1, B = 2, C = 3, D = 4 and E = 8, what is the answer to: $(A + B) \times D \div C?$

4 If A = 2, B = 3, C = 4, D = 5 and E = 6, what is the answer to: $(A \times D + E) \div C?$

5 If A = 2, B = 5, C = 6, D = 7 and E = 9, what is the answer to: $(C + D + B) \div A?$

6 If A = 2, B = 4, C = 5, D = 8 and E = 10, what is the answer to: $(A \times E) \div C + B?$

7 If A = 2, B = 3, C = 4, D = 5 and E = 12, what is the answer to: $(E \div B) \times A - D?$

8 If A = 2, B = 3, C = 4, D = 5 and E = 6, what is the answer to: $(B \times C + E) \div E?$

9 If A = 2, B = 4, C = 5, D = 6 and E = 8, what is the answer to: $(C \times D + A) \div B?$

10 If A = 2, B = 3, C = 4, D = 9 and E = 15, what is the answer to: $(E \times A - B) \div D?$

LESSON 13 PART 1: ANSWER SHEET

Mark your answer by putting a horizontal line in one of the boxes, as in the example below.

Example:

How Did You Do? Let's Find Out!

Here are the correct answers. You may mark your answers to these questions yourself.

1 D

2 E

3 D

4 C

5 E

6 D

7 B

8 B

9 E

10 B

If you scored 8 or more out of 10

This is great! Move on to the next set of questions and see if you can continue your good work. But do check over any questions you got wrong.

If you scored 5 to 7 out of 10

This score is okay but read this advice before moving on to the next set of questions.

Make sure you know your multiplication facts by heart – this will help you speed up on these questions.

If you scored fewer than 5 out of 10

Fewer than 5 is a score which you'll need to improve. Read the suggestions that follow before moving on to the next set of questions.

⇨ Do you understand what you have to do? If not, ask an adult to read the instructions and go through the example with you again.

⇨ Make sure you practise your addition, subtraction, multiplication and division.

⇨ Make sure you calculate each part of the equation in the correct order. Do the sums in brackets first, then multiplication and division and lastly addition and subtraction.

⇨ Look at the letter to number codes carefully each time. Sometimes the values aren't put in order of size.

LESSON 13 PART 2

My Time

My Score

Now look at these questions. Work out the sum, and mark the corresponding letter on the opposite page. Work quickly. You have 10 minutes to complete this task. Remember to get an adult to mark them for you.

1 If A = 1, B = 2, C = 3, D = 4 and E = 15, what is the answer to: $(A + B) + (C \times D)$?

2 If A = 2, B = 3, C = 4, D = 5 and E = 12, what is the answer to: $(A \times D - C) \div B$?

3 If A = 6, B = 2, C = 3, D = 4 and E = 8, what is the answer to: $(C \times E) \div D$?

4 If A = 2, B = 3, C = 4, D = 5 and E = 6, what is the answer to: $(E - D) + (C - B)$?

5 If A = 2, B = 5, C = 6, D = 8 and E = 9, what is the answer to: $(E \times D) - (C \times E) \div A$?

6 If A = 2, B = 4, C = 5, D = 8 and E = 10, what is the answer to: $(E - D) \times C \div A$?

7 If A = 2, B = 3, C = 4, D = 5 and E = 12, what is the answer to: $(E \div B) - (C \div A)$?

8 If A = 2, B = 5, C = 6, D = 60 and E = 50, what is the answer to: $A \times B \times C$?

9 If A = 42, B = 43, C = 5, D = 6 and E = 8, what is the answer to: $E \times D - C$?

10 If A = 2, B = 3, C = 5, D = 9 and E = 15, what is the answer to: $E \times B \div D$?

LESSON 13 PART 2: ANSWER SHEET

Mark your answer by putting a horizontal line in one of the boxes, as in the example below.

Example:

1

2

3

4

5

6

7

8

9

10

LESSON 14 Solving Coded Analogies

An analogy is when two or more things are related to each other in some way.

In this exercise you're given one, two or even three letters, and shown how these are turned into a code. You'll then use this information to work out the code for the second set of letters. Always remember that the two sets of letters should be turned into codes <u>in the same way</u>. Let's look at some examples.

A B C D E F G H I J K L M N O P Q R S T U V W X Y Z

Example 1

A is to B as   K is to?

Using the alphabet above you can see that to get from A to B you must count onwards one place along the alphabet from the first letter. This is your code and you must do the same for the second set. So now you should count on one place from the letter 'K', which is the letter <u>L</u>. You should mark this letter on your answer grid.

Example 2

CD is to FG as   MN is to?

In this example you have pairs of letters. Look at each letter on its own to start with. Again count how you got from the letter 'C' to 'F'. This is three jumps forward. Now you should check how you can get from the letter 'D' to 'G', and you find it's the same code (it isn't always, so be careful with these).

Now you need to solve the code for the second set of letters by counting on three places for each. You can see that MN becomes <u>PQ</u> so you should mark this on your answer grid.

HELPFUL HINTS

- Use the alphabet provided to help you – that's why it's there!

- Always work out the code from the first set of letters, and then apply it in the same way for the second set.

LESSON 14 PART 1

My Time

My Score

Now look at the questions below. Work them out as quickly as you can. There's an alphabet at the top of the page for you to use. You have 10 minutes to complete them all.

A B C D E F G H I J K L M N O P Q R S T U V W X Y Z

1 A is to C   as   H is to?

2 L is to Q   as   D is to?

3 S is to P   as   K is to?

4 A is to Z   as   C is to?

5 F is to K   as   Y is to?

6 AC is to DF   as   LN is to?

7 FE is to GD   as   TS is to?

8 HM is to FK   as   BG is to?

9 LO is to MQ   as   SV is to?

10 GI is to IJ   as   WY is to?

LESSON 14 PART 1: ANSWER SHEET

Mark your answer by putting a horizontal line in one of the boxes as in the examples below.

Example 1:

Example 2:

How Did You Do? Let's Find Out!

Here are the correct answers. You may mark your answers to these questions yourself.

1   J

2   I

3   H

4   X

5   D

6   OQ

7   UR

8   ZE

9   TX

10   YZ

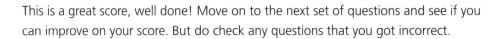

If you scored 8 or more out of 10

This is a great score, well done! Move on to the next set of questions and see if you can improve on your score. But do check any questions that you got incorrect.

If you scored 5 to 7 out of 10

Have a look at the following advice before moving on to the next set of questions.

⇨ I consider some of these questions to be quite simple while others can be tricky. Don't lose valuable time on one question if it's proving really tough, move on and go back to it once you've worked through the rest of the questions.

⇨ Make sure you count the differences between letters correctly. It's easy to make a mistake while doing this, so be careful.

If you scored fewer than 5 out of 10

Read the suggestions that follow before moving on to the next set of questions.

⇨ Do you understand what you have to do? If not, ask an adult to read the instructions and go through the examples with you again.

⇨ Make sure you work out the code by looking at the first set of letters and then apply the same method to the second set.

⇨ Remember to count the differences between letters carefully and to use the alphabet given to you to help with this.

Further hints

⇨ Draw a straight vertical line between the 'M' and 'N' on your alphabet. These are the middle two letters. This will help if you've got any mirror-type questions.

Mirror-type questions: These are questions that tend to use the extreme ends of the alphabet.

Example

A B C D E F G H I J K L M | N O P Q R S T U V W X Y Z

A is to Z as B is to?

In this example you shouldn't waste time counting between letters – instead you count in from each end of the alphabet. 'B' is the second letter in from the beginning so 'Y' is the correct answer because it's the second letter in from the end. Y is B's mirror letter. Watch out for these!

LESSON 14 PART 2

My Time

My Score

Now it's time to try some more of these questions. Work them out as quickly as you can. There's an alphabet at the top of the page for you to use. You have 10 minutes so work fast, and move on if you get stuck. You can always return to tricky questions at the end. Ask an adult to mark these for you.

A B C D E F G H I J K L M N O P Q R S T U V W X Y Z

1 B is to L   as   G is to?

2 M is to J   as   Y is to?

3 Q is to S   as   Z is to?

4 E is to V   as   H is to?

5 GF is to LK   as   PO is to?

6 MLK is to IHG   as   TSR is to?

7 SQ is to YW   as   LJ is to?

8 CF is to HK   as   MP is to?

9 NOP is to RST   as   VWX is to?

10 AE is to CG   as   KO is to?

LESSON 14 PART 2: ANSWER SHEET

Mark your answer by putting a horizontal line in one of the boxes, as in the examples below.

Example 1:

```
L  ▬
M  □
N  □
O  □
P  □
```

Example 2:

```
NO  □
OP  □
PQ  ▬
QR  □
RS  □
```

1

```
M  □
N  □
O  □
P  □
Q  □
```

2

```
U  □
V  □
W  □
X  □
Y  □
```

3

```
W  □
X  □
Y  □
A  □
B  □
```

4

```
R  □
S  □
T  □
U  □
V  □
```

5

```
TT  □
TU  □
UT  □
UU  □
VT  □
```

6

```
PQR  □
POR  □
POP  □
POS  □
PON  □
```

7

```
PR  □
RS  □
RQ  □
RP  □
QR  □
```

8

```
RT  □
RS  □
TR  □
TS  □
RU  □
```

9

```
XYZ  □
ABC  □
YZA  □
ZAB  □
BAZ  □
```

10

```
LP  □
LQ  □
MP  □
MQ  □
MR  □
```

VOCABULARY BUILDER 4
NEW WORDS

Use this page to write down any new words that you've learnt while reading this book. Use a dictionary to look up the meaning of each one.

New word	Meaning

LESSON 15 Finding Analogical Words

As we learnt in lesson 14, an analogy is when two or more things are related to each other in some way.

In this exercise you'll be given two groups of three words. You'll need to choose the two words that relate to the prompt words <u>in the same way</u>. If that sounds tricky, don't worry, these examples will help.

Example

green is to   (blue   colour   vegetables)

as snow is to   (weather   white   cold)

In this example you should begin by looking at the first prompt 'green is to' and the possible answers: blue, colour and vegetable. Work out how 'green' relates to these three words. Then do the same with the second prompt and the second set of words. Here goes:

1   Blue is also a colour, like green.

2   Colour tells you what group of words green belongs to.

3   Vegetable is an example of something that might be green.

Now look at the second set of words: 'snow is to'

1   Weather tells you what group of words snow belongs to.

2   White tells you what the colour of snow is.

3   Cold tells you what the temperature of snow is.

If you compare both sets you can see that **2** in the first set and **1** in the second describe the same relationship. They both tell you what group each word belongs to.

Your answers then should be <u>colour</u> and <u>weather</u>, and you should mark both of these on the answer grid.

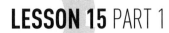

LESSON 15 PART 1

My Time		My Score	

Now look at the questions below. Work them out as quickly as you can. You have 10 minutes to complete them all. Remember to mark two answers on your answer grid – one word from each set in the question.

1 dog is to   (cat   puppy   fur)
    as lion is to   (cub   hunt   paw)

2 car is to   (park   steer   road)
    as ship is to   (sea   crew   captain)

3 nose is to   (face   smell   cold)
    as tongue is to   (taste   teeth   mouth)

4 curtain is to   (theatre   house   window)
    as carpet is to   (clean   floor   buy)

5 shout is to   (yell   angry   loud)
    as whisper is to   (scared   small   soft)

6 foot is to   (leg   body   toe)
    as hand is to   (shake   finger   watch)

7 wall is to   (building   tower   bricks)
    as window is to   (house   glass   break)

8 aunt is to   (insect   friend   uncle)
    as niece is to   (brother   good   nephew)

9 bird is to   (egg   wings   fly)
    as plant is to   (grow   seed   sun)

10 top is to   (high   above   bottom)
    as happy is to   (clever   sad   person)

LESSON 15 PART 1: ANSWER SHEET

Mark your answer by putting a horizontal line in one of the boxes for both sets of words for each answer, as in the example below.

Example:

blue ▢	weather ▬
colour ▬	white ▢
vegetable ▢	cold ▢

1

cat ▢	cub ▢
puppy ▢	hunt ▢
fur ▢	paw ▢

2

park ▢	sea ▢
steer ▢	crew ▢
road ▢	captain ▢

3

face ▢	taste ▢
smell ▢	teeth ▢
cold ▢	mouth ▢

4

theatre ▢	clean ▢
house ▢	floor ▢
window ▢	buy ▢

5

yell ▢	scared ▢
angry ▢	small ▢
loud ▢	soft ▢

6

leg ▢	shake ▢
body ▢	finger ▢
toe ▢	watch ▢

7

building ▢	house ▢
tower ▢	glass ▢
bricks ▢	break ▢

8

insect ▢	brother ▢
friend ▢	good ▢
uncle ▢	nephew ▢

9

egg ▢	grow ▢
wings ▢	seed ▢
fly ▢	sun ▢

10

high ▢	clever ▢
above ▢	sad ▢
bottom ▢	person ▢

How Did You Do? Let's Find Out!

Here are the two correct words for each answer. You may mark your answers to these questions yourself.

1 puppy, cub

2 road, sea

3 smell, taste

4 window, floor

5 loud, soft

6 toe, finger

7 bricks, glass

8 uncle, nephew

9 egg, seed

10 bottom, sad

If you scored 8 or more out of 10

This is terrific! Move on to the next set of questions and see if you can continue your good work. Make sure you understand why you got any answers incorrect.

If you scored 5 to 7 out of 10

Read this advice before moving on to the next set of questions.

⇨ I consider most of these questions to be quite simple but some can be tricky. You'll need to improve your score, but make sure you don't lose valuable time on a question if it's proving really tough. Move on and answer the other questions before coming back to it.

⇨ Make sure the relationship works for both sets of words.

If you scored fewer than 5 out of 10

You need to improve this score. Have another look at the questions and see if you can correct your answers before moving on to the next set of questions.

⇨ Do you understand what you have to do? If not, ask an adult to read the instructions and go through the examples with you again.

⇨ Make sure you understand how the words relate to one another, for example, are they:

- Opposite: as tall is to short

- Similar: as huge is to enormous

- Part of the other: as branch is to tree

- Made using the same letters: as bleat is to table

- The same word written backwards: as step is to pets

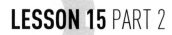

LESSON 15 PART 2

My Time

My Score

Now let's try some more. You have 10 minutes to complete them all, so work quickly. Remember to mark two answers on your answer grid – one word from each set in a question. Ask an adult to mark these for you.

1 teacher is to (paper   school   pupil)
    as doctor is to (coat   nurse   patient)

2 snake is to (poison   reptile   scales)
    as shark is to (sea   bite   fish)

3 glove is to (scarf   cold   hand)
    as sock is to (foot   warm   wool)

4 lion is to (pride   roar   run)
    as wolf is to (moon   pack   woods)

5 soldier is to (march   uniform   army)
    as sailor is to (ship   navy   sea)

6 football is to (net   goal   pitch)
    as tennis is to (lines   racquet   court)

7 triangle is to (three   acute   sides)
    as square is to (equal   four   cube)

8 bed is to (blanket   night   lay)
    as chair is to (table   sit   desk)

9 fire is to (logs   light   burn)
    as ice is to (cold   freeze   water)

10 film is to (rent   watch   enjoy)
    as book is to (read   write   open)

LESSON 15 PART 2: ANSWER SHEET

Mark your answer by putting a horizontal line in one of the boxes for both sets of words for each answer, as in the example below.

Example:

blue ☐	weather ⊟
colour ⊟	white ☐
vegetable ☐	cold ☐

1

paper ☐	coat ☐
school ☐	nurse ☐
pupil ☐	patient ☐

2

poison ☐	sea ☐
reptile ☐	bite ☐
scales ☐	fish ☐

3

scarf ☐	foot ☐
cold ☐	warm ☐
hand ☐	wool ☐

4

pride ☐	moon ☐
roar ☐	pack ☐
run ☐	woods ☐

5

march ☐	ship ☐
uniform ☐	navy ☐
army ☐	sea ☐

6

net ☐	lines ☐
goal ☐	racquet ☐
pitch ☐	court ☐

7

three ☐	equal ☐
acute ☐	four ☐
sides ☐	cube ☐

8

blanket ☐	table ☐
night ☐	sit ☐
lay ☐	desk ☐

9

logs ☐	cold ☐
light ☐	freeze ☐
burn ☐	water ☐

10

rent ☐	read ☐
watch ☐	write ☐
enjoy ☐	open ☐

SCORE SHEET

To find the percentage of a score out of 10, simply multiply your score by 10!

To find the average, add all your scores up and divide them by 15.

LESSON	Part 1 score	Part 1 percent	Part 2 score	Part 2 percent
1				
2				
3				
4				
5				
6				
7				
8				
9				
10				
11				
12				
13				
14				
15				
Average				

AND FINALLY...

Let me begin by saying 'Well done!' You must have worked hard to complete this book, especially on top of your homework from school!

Now that you've completed the first verbal reasoning book in the *Practise & Pass 11+* series, it's time to take stock. Have a look back at your scores and work out which questions you found quite straightforward and scored well on and which ones you found more difficult and didn't score so well on.

Make sure you read back over the methods for each question – these will serve you well during your examination. When you're ready, move on to the next book (*Practise & Pass 11+ Level Two: Develop Verbal Reasoning*), which features some more advanced versions of these and some more question types. In that book I also show you how to speed up your working using the answer grids.

Don't forget, if you need help with non-verbal reasoning, maths or English, there are *Practise & Pass 11+* books for each of those too to help you prepare for your exams:

⇨ *Practise & Pass 11+ Level One: Discover English*

⇨ *Practise & Pass 11+ Level One: Discover Maths*

⇨ *Practise & Pass 11+ Level One: Discover Non-Verbal Reasoning*

⇨ *Practise & Pass 11+ Level Two: Develop English*

⇨ *Practise & Pass 11+ Level Two: Develop Maths*

⇨ *Practise & Pass 11+ Level Two: Develop Non-Verbal Reasoning*

⇨ *Practise & Pass 11+ Level Two: Develop Verbal Reasoning*

⇨ *Practise & Pass 11+ Level Three: Practice Test Papers*

Keep working and good luck!

Vocabulary Builder 1 Answers
MISSING WORDS

1 The *builder* built a beautiful mansion.

2 The lucky *angler* landed an enormous fish.

3 The child was sick so he had to see the *doctor*.

4 The children listened carefully to their *teacher*.

5 The person who writes a book is called the book's *author*.

6 The *Prime Minister* is elected and leads the country.

7 The *sailor* brought his boat safely into the harbour.

8 Before an article is printed it must be checked by an *editor*.

9 The brave *fire fighter* helped put out the fire in the house.

10 The medical *registrar* helped the doctor to treat the patient.

Vocabulary Builder 2 Answers
PROBLEMS TO SOLVE

1 All the words contain names of trees:
   a) spl*ash*
   b) cr*oak*
   c) h*elm*et
   d) f*ir*st
   e) s*pine*
   f) f*ig*ure
   g) st*eak*

2 Since the fox can never be left alone with one duck and the boat cannot power itself, the order should be…

Duck A and duck B row across to the other side. Duck B stays on the bank while Duck A returns. Duck A now stays on the starting bank while the fox rows across alone. The fox stays on the far bank while duck B returns alone with the boat and picks up duck A. Now both ducks cross the river together and rejoin the fox.

Answers To Part 2 Questions

LESSON 1

1. coat ripped,   trip
2. new hat,   what
3. with interest,   thin
4. while addressing, lead
5. outside all,   deal
6. what extent,   text
7. while after,   leaf
8. lamb entered,   bent
9. door opened,   rope
10. we are,   wear

LESSON 2

1. ALL, BALLOON
2. RID, BRIDGE
3. RIG, FRIGHTENED
4. OFF, OFFICE
5. ONE, TELEPHONE
6. RAG, GARAGE
7. WON, WONDERFUL
8. RAW, DRAWING
9. USE, HOUSE
10. IRE, TIRED

LESSON 3

1. l, pump, flight
2. c, rate, clock
3. t, read, weight
4. r, ride, grown
5. d, rain, band
6. g, thin, glean
7. i, plan, noise
8. k, chin, linked
9. m, able, clamp
10. s, tale, boots

LESSON 4

1. g, wing, ghost
2. r, glider, reach
3. w, now, when
4. t, weight, track
5. a, rota, amount
6. s, works, stalk
7. y, storey, years
8. n, flown, neat
9. f, beef, flock
10. h, bath, height

LESSON 5

1. y, ploy, yelp, clay, yacht
2. r, spur, rice, tour, rage
3. g, rung, gift, fang, gnaw
4. e, lute, earl, gate, ever
5. l, pill, leaf, seal, lore
6. d, heed, down, seed, daze
7. n, turn, nave, twin, nook
8. b, slab, book, swab, bull
9. t, rift, town, flit, twig
10. h, lush, high, loch, hoot

LESSON 6

1. green house, greenhouse
2. bit ten,   bitten
3. car pet,   carpet
4. pend ant,   pendant
5. cart ridge,   cartridge
6. in stead,   instead
7. pass age,   passage
8. rat her,   rather
9. sea side,   seaside
10. back ward,   backward

LESSON 7

1. level   plane
2. hurry   hasten
3. gasp   pant
4. park   estate
5. foggy   murky
6. escape   dodge
7. donate   pledge
8. count   record
9. buckle   clasp
10. ancient   olden

LESSON 8

1. well	amazing
2. I	my
3. round	two
4. fire	fearsome
5. blared	the (2nd)
6. lightning	thunder
7. his	studied
8. precariously	helicopter
9. dwelled	deep
10. Its	it's

LESSON 9

1. C
2. P
3. FO
4. O
5. H
6. X
7. P
8. J
9. JMP
10. R

LESSON 10

1. SLING
2. GATE
3. SINGLE
4. ENLIST
5. JSOM
6. JMIHO
7. MOIJ

8. CALLER
9. FEAR
10. CARER

LESSON 11

1. 19 B 6 F
2. CAKE
3. MOOD
4. GNHIY
5. GDE
6. CZOC
7. GQRX
8. 18 1 7 19
9. HAABPCPDYE
10. CMDP

LESSON 12

1. 18
2. 46
3. 4
4. 32
5. 13
6. 12
7. 385
8. 13.8
9. 49
10. 24

LESSON 13

1. E
2. A
3. A

4. A
5. E
6. C
7. A
8. D
9. B
10. C

LESSON 14

1. Q
2. V
3. B
4. S
5. UT
6. PON
7. RP
8. RU
9. ZAB
10. MQ

LESSON 15

1. pupil	patient
2. reptile	fish
3. hand	foot
4. pride	pack
5. army	navy
6. pitch	court
7. three	four
8. sleep	sit
9. burn	freeze
10. watch	read